**Missouri Center
for the Book**

ಜಜಜ

**Missouri Authors
Collection**

Today's Game

Other novels by Martin Quigley

Winners and Losers

The Secret Project of Sigurd O'Leary

A Tent on Corsica

9C
C
ui

T⚾day's Game

A NOVEL BY Martin Quigley

Martin Quigley (signature)

New York · The Viking Press

Second Printing, November, 1966

Copyright © 1965 by Martin Quigley
All rights reserved

First published in 1965 by The Viking Press, Inc.
625 Madison Avenue, New York, N.Y. 10022

Published simultaneously in Canada by
The Macmillan Company of Canada Limited

Library of Congress catalog card number: 65-16901
Printed in the United States of America

With Many Thanks
to

Bing Devine
Johnny Keane
Joe McShane
Jim Toomey
Bill White
Del Wilber

BLUE JAYS ROSTER

7 Mann, mgr.

Coaches

41 Cronkite   27 Tate
40 Moore   3 Wolf

	Age	Bats	Throws	Pct.
Infielders				
17 Brooks	25	R	R	.278
18 Messengale	20	L	L	.333
4 Norman	36	L	L	.342
2 Sandowski	34	L	R	.302
12 Tuffson	25	R	R	.267
6 Wade	30	R	R	.331
3 Wolf	39	L	R	.284
Outfielders				
8 Crum	42	L	R	.192
11 J. Jones	26	R	R	.283
15 T. Jones	33	L-R	L	.275
10 Wellington	24	R	R	.197
16 Wilkins	26	L	R	.279
Catchers				
1 Caluga	36	L	R	.225
14 Michaels	23	L	R	.110
5 Slater	37	L	R	.264
Pitchers				
22 Anderson	26	R	R	W2-L3
20 Baxley	34	L	L	W6-L2
25 Cruise	38	L	R	W1-L1
32 Henry	28	R	L	W0-L0
23 Kerwin	31	R	R	W2-L2
26 Kunz	30	R	L	W1-L3
30 Martin	22	R	R	W1-L3
28 Murdock	25	L	L	W2-L4
24 Pasquale	24	R	R	W2-L0
21 Sholey	29	L	L	W3-L4

9 Briscoe, mgr.

Coaches

34 Kista	32 Smith	
33 Quist	35 Wilkinson	

	Age	Bats	Throws	Pct.
Infielders				
2 Amacito	27	L	L	.215
11 Branstadt	23	L	R	.306
3 Fisk	31	R	R	.265
1 Hochstein	28	L	R	.289
8 McStay	26	R	R	.261
4 Sorenson	32	L	R	.287
Outfielders				
5 Ates	25	L	R	.269
21 Black	31	R	R	.298
25 Conrad	36	L	L	.262
20 Perdowski	27	R	R	.258
14 Shassere	30	R	R	.255
7 Shepley	29	L	R	.314
Catchers				
36 Anderson	30	R	R	.256
10 Costello	36	R	R	.240
15 Oppenheim	24	L	R	.267
Pitchers				
38 Adams	37	R	R	W8-L1*
12 Benz	31	L	R	W2-L2
37 Gonzales	32	L	L	W4-L1
16 Higgins	29	R	L	W4-L3
44 Johnson	21	R	R	W1-L0
19 McDonald	36	L	L	W4-L3
30 Massucci	26	R	R	W3-L3
26 Nicholson	22	R	R	W5-L3
24 Randolph	28	L	L	W2-L1
29 Wilson	22	R	R	W2-L3

* Adams W4-L1 while with Blue Jays.

BLUE JAYS VS. WARRIORS

Sunday, June 9
Probable Starting Line-ups

BLUE JAYS			WARRIORS		
17	Brooks, 2B	.278	1	Hochstein, 2B	.289
6	Wade, ss	.331	21	Black, CF	.298
10	Wellington, LF	.197	7	Shepley, RF	.314
4	Norman, 1B	.342	4	Sorenson, 3B	.287
15	T. Jones, RF	.275	2	Amacito, 1B	.215
12	Tuffson, 3B	.267	5	Ates, LF	.269
16	Wilkins, CF	.279	20	Perdowski, LF	.258
5	Slater, C	.264	8	McStay, ss	.261
20	Baxley, P	6 - 2	36	Anderson, C	.256
			15	Oppenheim, C	.267
			38	Adams, P	8 - 1

HOW THEY STAND

(Not including last night's games)

TEAM	W	L	PCT.	GB
Warriors	31	19	.620	——
Dodgers	30	22	.577	2
Cubs	27	22	.551	3½
Reds	27	23	.540	4
Blue Jays	24	23	.511	5½
Pirates	24	24	.500	6
Phillies	23	27	.460	8
Braves	22	27	.449	8½
Astros	21	30	.412	10½
Mets	20	32	.385	12

Today's Game

1

His first thought of the morning was his last thought of the previous night: I should have squeezed it home.

The sleeping pill had worn off, and there was no natural sleep for him. Last night's defeat was in his mouth, and his losing streak was in his belly. His stomach was churning acid; it needed bread and milk.

His losing streak was sure good for the milkman.

Marianna was sleeping. Her blonded hair and the depth of the pillow concealed her face and made him feel already alone with today. If I'd only squeezed it home last night, he thought, I would have come home to a winner's drinks, steak, and bed, and I'd be waking up now thinking how can they beat a smart, lucky player like me. He had come home a loser in extra innings to a wife whose best treatment was to leave him alone, and a sleeping pill. If I'd only . . . Next kid we get, I'm going to name her Ida Only. Ida Only Mann, daughter of Barney Mann, the former major-league . . .

He eased out of bed and out of the room, closing the door silently behind him. The thick carpeting, wall to wall in every room of the house except the kitchen and baths, told his bare feet to remind him that he was playing every game now for the alienable right to keep paying for a $46,000 four-bedroom home on which he still owed $18,000. On the way to the bathroom he passed the bedroom in which Marjie and Sally, their four- and six-year olds, lay like storybook fairies on their cool beds and, across the hall, the bedroom in which Sue was in her own secret world of fourteen. His wife and children, the luxury of his home, and the quiet Sunday morning had nothing to do with what he must do this day.

It was just after seven-thirty. In the kitchen he fetched a bottle of milk from the refrigerator and a glass from the cupboard and went out into the patio in his pajamas and settled in one of the lawn chairs by the redwood picnic table. The patio, topped by the leaves of an old oak, was screened by fence and shrubs. The morning was decorated with dew, the fragrance of flowers, and the songs of birds, but its loveliness was not of him or for him. He was spading up the details of last night's game. His concentration was so intense that he would be able ten years later to call up the names and potentialities of every lefthanded batter Briscoe had on his bench in the eleventh, the count on Wellington when he went after that outside curve in the tenth. . . .

Marjie, hardly awake, came staggering out into the sunshine and ran to him with little yelps. He picked her up and held her close, feeling awakeness moving through her body as her arms tightened around his neck. His concern for his mistakes of the night before spread into a dull ache of despair for his future. He was forty-two years old and somehow had to make a living for Marianna and the girls for the next twenty years or so as a baseball man. He knew nothing else. He had been making his living in and at baseball since the age of eighteen, and he had come all the way up to big-league manager, whence there was no place but thence. He had been promoted from coach to manager after the all-star game last summer, and he had brought the club from a fading sixth place to a strong third. He had got off to a good start this season and was in first place by the middle of May. Then after the big trade, Wellington for Adams even—the trade he had asked for— he could not win for losing. He had lost twelve out of fifteen and nine in a row, and had sunk from first place to a sinking fifth.

Maybe I'm not as quick and bright as I used to be, he thought, hugging his daughter. Maybe those Seconal pills Doc gave me to sleep make me stupid when I'm awake. Maybe they sap my confidence. I should have played my hunch and squeezed it home.

"Are we going to the zoo today, Daddy?" his daughter asked, wriggling out of his hard hug.

"Tomorrow. Daddy has to work today. Tomorrow you and I and Sally will go to the zoo and ride the train and see the seals and the polar bears."

"You have to go to the ball park today," she said knowingly.

He nodded and kissed her forehead. "Daddy has to work today."

"But not on the road?"

"Not for another whole week." He had played and lost eight games on this home stand. Unless he started winning, Mike would have to try someone else. This house and their life here, where they were taking root, would go down the drain with the lost games.

He poured a glass of milk and held it for Marjie, who turned her head away. So he raised it to her, said, "First today," and drank it down. "Let's you and me have breakfast outside."

They carried oranges and cereal and bread, butter, and jelly out to the redwood table, and he made a pot of tea for himself. They made a fine picnic breakfast. He lit a cigar and sat back in the sunshine and watched his daughter fly on her swing through its smoke, singing songs of swinging while he thought thoughts of losing.

Today's would be Jerry Adams' first game against him since he had traded Jerry for Bill Wellington. Jerry's family was still living down the street in a house like this. He and Jerry had been on the club together for fifteen years. Marianna and Susie Adams were—had been—best friends, and their kids had sat together in Section P. Jerry and his family had put down roots here—the hopeful, tentative roots of baseball families—but now they would have to sell out and move into a rented house, most likely, on the Coast. A thirty-seven-year-old pitcher, even a sure Hall-of-Famer like Jerry, cannot take on a twenty-year mortgage on the basis of job security.

Today Jerry would be out there firing to prove that Barney had done a rotten personal thing and a stupid baseball thing to trade the most effective righthanded pitcher in baseball—this year and maybe next—for a young Negro outfielder who still had his ability and himself to prove and who was proving neither. Baseball is a game of sentiment.

He felt the aloneness of being on a losing ball club. When you were losing, you were lonely people. Every player was devoted to the big thing, the team and winning, but, with every game lost, each player became concerned less with losing as a team and concerned more with not losing as a person. Each player became a lost bit of team, concentrating on making his own plays but sure in his bones that he or somebody else would kick the game away. Their fearless leader was paid to give them the loose and eager feeling, one and all, that they were a team of confident players who could play over any mistake any one of them might make. But right now their fearless leader was as alone and unsure as any of them—except Wellington. Who could be as alone as Wellington? Baseball is a game of sentiment. It makes you choke up to think about it.

"C'mon in and get a decent breakfast and have some coffee with me." It was Marianna from the patio door. "And, Marjie, you come in and start getting your Sunday-school clothes on."

"Right away in a minute." His voice seemed high-pitched and strained. Would it sound that way in the clubhouse and the dugout? "You get in like your mother said," he told Marjie, because he wanted to be alone a minute before he put on his winning smile.

Why do I do what I do and care so much? There must be some way to make myself believe it's just a game played with a ball. He threw the useless thought and his cigar away and got up and walked into the kitchen, smiling. He picked up Sally, the six-year-old, and gave her a swing and a hug.

"I'm sorry you lost again last night, Daddy."

And Sue (named for Susie Adams, because she and Marianna had been best friends) hugged his neck. She couldn't be fourteen. "Here's a kiss for good luck, Daddy. I know you're going to win today."

"That's going to do it," he said, snapping his fingers.

"Sue, see that the kids get dressed and ready to go. Sally should have a bath. I gave Marjie one last night."

"I want a bath too."

"Okay, you can have one too, Marjie," Sue said and took them to their bedroom.

"I've soft-boiled you three eggs, and I want you to eat them. You can't have nothing on your stomach all day."

"I had some cereal, but I'm still hungry," he said, lying.

"That tenth inning was really rough," she said, as if she were putting a poultice on a boil to draw it out of him now that it was daylight and a new day. "A man on third with nobody out, and they let him die there." They had failed to score in the tenth and had lost it in the eleventh on Cheese Sorenson's home run.

"*I* let him die there," he said. "I had a hunch to squeeze that run home, but I didn't play my hunch."

"Squeeze it home!" she protested. "You've got the top of your order coming up, and no outs, and you're going to squeeze it home!"

"Briscoe the Bear played it just right, and Barney the Boob played it all wrong."

"What did Barney the Boob do wrong? Should he have gone to the plate and hit the long fly ball himself?"

"Not one manager in a hundred would have played it the way Briscoe did, and I should have been the one manager in a thousand to counter his play with a squeeze bunt."

In their tenth, Pasquale, his brilliant righthanded relief pitcher, had sliced a fly ball into the right-field corner and had raced all the way to third; it looked as if they were home free. Brooks, Wade, and Wellington, three righthanded batters, were coming up against Briscoe's righthanded reliefer.

"What ninety-nine managers in a hundred would have done was walk Brooks and Wade to load the bases, bring in the outfield, and set up the force-out at home and the double play."

Marianna nodded. "When he didn't, I thought he had given away his best chance."

Barney shook his head. "That's what I was hoping he would do, because that would bring up Wellington, Norman, and Jones. Then all we need is a hit or a fly ball from Wellington or Big Don or a base hit from Jones. But the last thing Briscoe wants is to see Big Don come up there with less than two outs, so he decides to pitch to Brooks and get him out on the ground."

"Which he does."

"That hasn't happened yet. When I see that he is pitching to Brooks, I see it as clear then as I do now that my best chance is to squeeze it home. All I've got to do is touch my cap and rub my nose. But I don't do it. I never squeeze with no outs. Who does? But I should have made the play. Timmy is a good bunter, and Pasquale is one of my fastest runners."

"Why didn't you do it, Barney?"

"I lost my nerve," he said.

"Oh, Barney," Marianna said from the stove.

"I can justify it. Nobody can fault me on it. Brooks is hitting well, and Briscoe has his outfield in—so I let him swing away."

"One out," Marianna said.

"Now Wade is up there, righthander against right-hander, but I don't have a lefthanded batter on the bench that I'd rather see at the plate in his place."

"He happens to be hitting three-thirty," Marianna put in.

Barney nodded. "And he can hit the fly ball. My nose began to itch, but I let him hit away."

"He fouled it straight up. Two out."

"Now I've got to go with Wellington."

"Who hasn't hit the ball out of the infield in a week."

"He's the best young hitter in baseball."

"But a righthander against a righthander. You've got Crum on the bench."

Dandy Crum was an aging ageless Negro who had wasted five thousand base hits in Negro ball before somebody gave him the chance upstairs.

"Why didn't you come with Dandy, Barney? Or Wolf? Or Sandowski?"

"It would show I've got no confidence in Wellington."

"Which you don't."

"He's my left fielder. I've got to give him a chance to battle out of it. I've got a big investment in him."

"You sure have."

Marianna was a pretty, sharp-featured Southern hill girl, tough and emotional. She had hardly spoken to him for a week after he had traded her best friend out of her life for a Negro ballplayer. She was one of many who thought he had also traded away his clear shot at a pennant this year. It was her home, too.

Wellington had looked at a fast strike, taken a curve outside, and looked at another fast strike. "I had a hunch to let Dandy go up with two strikes, but I didn't play that one either," Barney said. The one-two pitch was an outside curve, but Wellington, afraid that he would go down with his bat on his shoulder, chased it.

"And fouled it ninety feet to the first baseman," Marianna said. "Now what about his confidence?"

"He ain't got any."

"You better stick to playing your hunches, honey. Besides, they're not really hunches. You think so fast they just seem like hunches. Eat your eggs before they get cold. I put lots of butter in them, and they'll keep your stomach from riling up."

The phone was ringing, and Sue called down the hall that it was for Daddy. It was a visiting sportswriter named Jim Paulson, in town to wind up a story for *Sports Illustrated* on the Adams-Wellington trade.

"You don't want to talk to me, Mr. Paulson. You want to talk to Mike Brandt. I work for him."

"I've talked to Mike, Barney. He said you had convinced him that the trade would keep your club in contention."

When you are losing, every person is a lost bit of team. Barney rubbed his nose with his free hand. Mike did not interfere with the way he ran the club on the field, and now Mike wasn't interfering with the way he ran his mouth about this trade. He had to keep in mind that what he said now would be in print either after his losing streak was a memory or after he was a memory. "He didn't say whether or not he was still convinced, did he?"

It got the laugh from Paulson and threw him off his stride. "He said the answer was whether or not you stayed in contention."

"I sure agree with that." He needed time to think. "It's nothing I'd care to discuss on the phone, Mr. Paulson."

"Today's game is the big one. Can you give me some time alone before the game? I'm on a tight deadline. I've got to file my story right afterwards."

"Today's game is one game out of one hundred and sixty-two league games we will play this year. I don't see that today's game will have too much to do with it."

"Everybody seems to think today's game is kind of a showdown."

"Talk to everybody who thinks so."

"You don't?"

"I asked for this trade with the over-all strength of the club in mind, Mr. Paulson. I think we're in contention now, and I think we'll be in contention after today's game."

"There are other angles I'd like to discuss. Such as the fact that you and Jerry were best friends for years."

"Like I said, it's nothing I care to discuss on the

phone. Tell you what, Mr. Paulson, I'm not leaving for the park for another hour or so. If you were to grab a cab and come out here, Marianna would fix you some breakfast and I'd be glad to give you my views on this particular trade—about twenty minutes' worth."

"Fair enough. Appreciate it, Barney. Tell Marianna I've had breakfast but would enjoy a cup of coffee."

He went back into the kitchen and told Marianna that they were having company. He would shower and shave while he thought up what not to tell the press.

"Do you have to talk to him now?"

"It's part of the job." Maybe my next job.

Looking at his mirrored face, sunburned and lined from squinting and worrying in his healthful outdoor job, he could see that it still belonged to the lanky, confident, fast-talking scrapper he used to be.

When he got through dressing, Paulson was drinking coffee with Marianna in the living room. "I'll leave you boys with it," she said.

"I don't have much time, so I'll tell you my reasons," Barney said directly. "When the season got under way, we knew that some of the kids we had hoped would give us solid outfield strength were not ready for this season. We knew that we needed a strong righthanded hitter in the outfield if we were going to make a real run for it. If you don't have what you need in baseball, you got to trade for it. We wanted Wellington."

"We?"

"When I say we, I mean me. Yes, I wanted Wellington. I wanted him for his power, for his speed, for his arm, and for his youth. They needed a stopper on their pitching staff. They wanted Adams as bad as I wanted Wellington. They wouldn't listen to anybody but Adams, and we offered them some fancy combinations. I wouldn't listen to anybody but Wellington, and they offered some fancy combinations.

"I've got a strong pitching staff—the strongest in the league, in my opinion. I needed that righthanded power and speed and arm. I knew I was giving up the best pitcher in baseball, this year, to get Wellington. Wellington will give me power and the threat of power every day. Adams will give me twenty wins, of which I will get maybe twelve by using one of my other pitchers. In other words, Adams—without Wellington—is worth eight games to me. So what it comes down to is, is Wellington worth more than eight games to me? I ask you, is a guy who his first full season was a three-hundred hitter, a hundred and ten runs batted in, thirty home runs, twenty stolen bases—and righthanded so everybody in the league doesn't have an old lefthander on his staff who makes his living beating you—is he worth eight games? In my opinion, he was and he is. I'm talking about this season. Not to mention that Wellington is twenty-four and Adams is thirty-seven."

Paulson had been making notes. "A lot of baseball people agree with you. Many don't. It's the most controversial trade in a long time."

Barney shrugged. "That's not a question, so I don't have to answer it."

"Without Adams, do you think you still have the best pitching staff in the league?"

"You can't give up Adams and not be hurt. I'd say with Adams we had the best. Without Adams, we've got one of the best, maybe as good as any of the other two or three clubs with top strength."

"So far the trade hasn't worked out for you, has it?"

"I think it will."

"But it hasn't."

"Wellington's in a slump, and the club is in a losing streak."

"How much has Wellington's slump contributed to the losing streak?"

"If he had been hitting up to normal, we would not have lost nine games in a row."

"How many games has his slump cost you of that nine?"

"I would say that if he had been hitting three hundred instead of about three hundredths, and considering the opportunities he has had to drive in runs, that we probably would have won three or four of them."

"You think he'll pull out of it?"

"Certainly. Bill has only one fault. He cares too much, and he's trying too hard. He feels he's cost us all nine games, not just half of them. He knows we gave a Hall-of-Fame pitcher for him. I can't tell him relax, don't care. I can't tell him how to hit. Don Norman can't tell him how to hit. He's got to battle out of it, and I know he will. He's a fine young fellow with a deep sense of personal and team responsibility."

"Do you think he'll hit Adams today?"

Last year, in twenty-one times against Adams, Wellington had hit one home run, two doubles, and four singles, for a precise .333 average. In addition, he had been walked once and been hit by a pitch once. Of the twelve outs, he had struck out four times, grounded out five times (twice into double plays), and flied out three times. Barney said, "I haven't checked the figures, but my impression is that he hit Adams about as well as any other right-hander in the league."

"How about today?"

"The way he's been going, he couldn't hit Sam Sausage, let alone Jerry Adams."

"You're going to play him?"

"I haven't made out my line-up card yet."

"Adams was real popular on your club, Barney. Isn't it a fact that some of the Old Line resented the trade a great deal?"

Some of them hated his guts for it—Slater, Jones, and Wolf, probably Big Don Norman too—the proud Old Line of the great championship club. They believed that it was a bad trade for this year and next, and they did not have many years after this year and next. But they also thought that Jerry had earned a permanent place with the organization—coach, scout, minor-league manager, front office—or the right, in any case, to make a secondary career here where he was best known and had good connections, and where his family was taking root. Barney said, "I suppose some of them think I made a dumb trade. He's a great guy as well as a great pitcher. We all hated to see him go."

"Don't you think that this feeling—whatever it is—might have something to do with your losing streak?"

The Old Liners were not giving Wellington and some of the other kids, especially Timmy Brooks and Dee Wilkins, any feeling that they belonged on the club. "Of course not. Every one of my people is a major-leaguer, and every one is putting out one hundred per cent."

"What about reports that there is some resentment among the Old Liners that you got the manager's job over Granny Wolf?"

One of his mistakes had been in keeping Granny on as a player-coach. Granny had been team captain for ten years, through the great years. Mike had chosen him, Barney, over Granny because Granny believed that there was another championship left in the Old Line. When asked, Barney had told Mike that he thought that Slater and Norman and an infusion of young ballplayers would give them the best chance this year and as a contending club for years to come. You had to clear out the old wood to let the young trees grow.

"Granny is a fine coach. We get along as well now as when I was at short and he was at second."

Thinking that he might be out of a job by the time his words were in print and that his own people would be reading them if he were still in uniform, he said: "This is a very close ball club. The kids look up to the Old Liners, and they are doing everything they can to help bring the kids along." Like turning their backs on them in the clubhouse.

"Everything I hear, those kids of yours would lie down and die for you."

"If they love me that much, let 'em git up and git goin' for me."

"I understand you and Jerry were very close personal friends." Paulson folded his note paper to a fresh side and waited.

They had played ball together all season and gone pheasant-hunting and played golf together in the fall. They went out together on the road and played cards with their wives at home. Barney had stood up for Jerry at his wedding. Jerry had named his first boy for Barney, and Barney had named his first girl for Jerry's wife. "That's right," Barney said.

"Where does that stand?"

"He's with his club, and I'm with mine."

"You didn't let your personal feelings stand in the way of the trade."

"Is that a question?"

"Call it a question."

"I'm a baseball man."

"They say he's pretty bitter about you and the trade."

"I don't blame him for thinking I made a bad trade."

"This won't be a routine game for him."

"He's a baseball man too."

"Do you think the trade had anything to do with bringing on your losing streak?"

"No."

"What did?"

"Bad luck and bad breaks—more than our share."

Paulson made his notes and looked away.

Barney continued. "I've told you how much Wellington's slump has hurt us. It's also true that Adams, pitching the way he has, would have won an additional two, maybe three, of those games for us. But the slump or loss of an individual player doesn't hurt a ball club as much as a streak of bad luck. Luck and the breaks—good and bad—run in streaks in baseball the way they do in cards or dice. In the last few weeks we've had more than our share of bad breaks.

"Take Don Norman. Friday night he hit a ball as hard as a human being can hit a ball—a line drive four hundred feet to the center fielder. In the first game of this home stand, against the Reds, he hit a ball into the upper stands that I saw hit the foul line. Everybody in the park saw it hit the foul line except the man who called the play, Biggie Lund, umpiring at first base. Both times we've got the third out instead of the ball game. That's the way it's been."

"Take last night. You can't get a fly ball with a man on third and nobody out," Paulson said.

"Yeah," Barney said. "And the club tries harder and tenses up."

"What do you do about it?"

"Battle along till something breaks the spin."

"Is today the day? Everybody seems to have the notion that today is the day that will tell the story."

"That's the first question you asked."

"Just another game?"

"I want this game as much as I've ever wanted a game in my life, player or manager." He watched Paulson write down the words. Next thing you knew, he would be telling the whole truth. He got up. "Okay? I've got to be getting out to the ball park."

Paulson closed his notebook. "How's chances catching a ride out with you?"

"I know this is going to sound rude to you, Mr. Paulson, but no. I've got some questions of my own to answer, and I can't think about your questions and mine at the same time."

"What kind of questions?"

"Like how to beat Jerry Adams."

At the door Paulson offered his hand. "I know a lot of people are hoping you'll fall on your cocky face, but I happen to be a fan as well as a writer. It won't affect what I write, but I hope you beat his brains out today."

"May I ask you a question, Mr. Paulson?"

"Jim."

"The question I want to ask you, Jim, is this: why do you and all the millions of people of America who don't have a damn thing at stake, not even a two-dollar bet, why do you care so much about something that is just a game played for your amusement? It happens to be my life and my job, so I got some reason to care, but why do you?"

"It's my job too."

"I mean why do you care as a fan? Why do you hope I beat Jerry Adams' brains out? I'm a guy with a number on his back, and so is he."

They had stepped out onto the porch, and Paulson swept his long fingers through his short hair and stood slouched, inhaling smoke into his deflated lungs. He threw the cigarette away, and his hands moved down his chest and seemed to support his belly. He was a man of thought who had never performed in any arena. He was an asker, not an answerer.

"I mean," Barney said, "why do people care so much who wins a ball game?"

Paulson found a cigarette and lit it and blew smoke toward his skinny legs and big feet. Suddenly he began to speak. "I've thought about that for a long time, Barney. It's because we know what the game is and who you are. We sit in the stands and look down and watch you struggle, man against man, and man against the fates. Perhaps you are to us what the demi-gods and heroes were to the ancient Greeks, and perhaps baseball is to us what their theater was to them—a drama with familiar heroes in familiar situations."

"Like the gladiators?"

Paulson shook his head. "No, it's a different thing."

"But me? Why me over Jerry Adams? He's a real hero."

"We see ourselves in our heroes," Paulson said and walked away. "Good luck, Barney."

His flock of girls was all ladied-up for Sunday school. "That sportswriter said I was a regular Greek hero, something on the order of Achilles or Hercules," he told them.

"We'll pray that you win today, Daddy," Sue said.

"And that we have a nice day for the zoo tomorrow," Sally added.

He raised his hands as if stopping a base runner. "The Adams kids will be praying *their* daddy wins, and the farmers will be praying for rain." As an Air Force gunner in the war, he had thought much about prayer and had gone from the notion that it was an ineffective and belittling form of personal protection to the conclusion that it was asking for trouble. He did not want his kids to jinx him by praying for him. "Pray something big," he said, "like there won't be another war and that the Lord giveth and the Lord taketh away. God doesn't care who wins ball games or who has sunny days for the zoo." He hugged them and patted their rumps.

"You kids get out to the station wagon, we'll be late," Marianna commanded.

"You'll be driving out today?" Barney asked his wife.

"I don't want to hang around the park waiting for

you if we lose," she said. Now that she was a manager's wife, she had a box of her own, which she had chosen, against the screen behind home plate, where she could concentrate on the game and keeping her own score without people trampling in front of her. Sometimes she took friends, but since the losing streak she had gone to the games alone.

"I'll get home early," he said, "unless Mike wants a conference."

"Have you got your line-up set for today?"

"I'm thinking about it."

"Have you thought about starting the Old Liners against Jerry?"

Automatically he said, "Wolf for Brooks at second, Sandowski for Tuffson at third, Ted Jones for Jeff Jones in right . . ."

"They hit left, and they've got a better chance of getting you some runs against Jerry than those green righthanded kids."

"It might be the best way to win today's game," he admitted.

"Think about it," she insisted. "Experience and lefthanded power."

"My trouble is that I think."

"You're thinking that if you go with the Old Liners you'll be admitting you've been wrong going with your kids."

"You're an Old Liner at heart."

"I wish we had Jerry going for us today instead of against us." She came to him and kissed him. "Good luck out there today."

To hear her say it made him more alone and stronger.

2

Marianna was wrong about what she was right about. If he went with the Old Liners, they would go out all charged up to defeat him, Barney, by beating their old buddy, Jerry. His kids, if he started them, would go out there with so much to lose they would lose. (Would the Old Liners give away more runs in the field than they would bring home at the plate?) But if he won today with the Old Liners, he would have a shot club for the rest of the season. Win or lose today with the kids, he had a chance of making a winning team out of them.

"Good morning, Mr. Filo." It was Edgar, the Negro attendant for the parking lot for club personnel just across from the clubhouse entrance. Barney got out of the car and stretched himself for a moment in the sunshine. There were two or three thousand fans shuffling on the sidewalks to the ticket windows or standing in clusters, tickets in hand, hashing out the day's chances. There was showdown in the air, as there was before big games. The fans knew.

He was about to begin a day's work that had begun twenty-four years before when, in 1940, just out of high school and American Legion baseball, he had signed with Mike, then a front-office assistant to Old Dud Dudley, for no bonus and twenty dollars a week to play for Crookston in the Northern League, Class D. The day would end when he died. He saw in Edgar's loving brown eyes that there was no life for a baseball man except in baseball. He stretched again in the sunshine. "Whattaya say, Edgar?"

"I say we're gonna pull out today, Mr. Filo." Filo was an accounting term meaning First In, Last Out, that Edgar had picked up at night school during two years of hard effort before the white world had put him back in his place. He shared with Barney his secret accounting names for several of the team: Fifo for Dee Wilkins, who came early to jog himself loose and was out of the clubhouse and being driven away in his convertible by his current girl before the rest of them had their socks off; Liso for Big Don Norman, Last In, Second Out. . . .

"Our losing streak hasn't hurt attendance—yet," Barney remarked.

"The people are gonna fill those right-field stands today," Edgar said. "We're with *you*, Mr. Filo."

They stood in easy intimacy, men of the game together, each aware that the other was not responsible for opened doors and closed gates. The Negro world was with Barney. From the day he had slid hard into rookie Jackie Robinson at second and then given him a hand up, the Negro fans had been with Barney. Now Wellington's slump was an intense and personal matter to them.

"I want him to make it too," Barney said.

Edgar was not aware, either, that Wellington's name had not been spoken between them. "You're the man can help him."

Barney put out his hand. "Gimme five for luck, Edgar." He crossed the street, smiling but not pausing, as the throng of autograph kids came running. He passed out cards with his printed picture and autograph and kept walking through the clubhouse door, which the guard opened for him and closed upon the clamoring fans.

Hurry Harry Honicker, the clubhouse boy of sixty-five, was shining the shoes of the stars. Mel, the batboy, was toiling with bats and helmets. "Morning, boys," Barney said, noting that the recreation room to the left was unoccupied. To the right, in the training room at the end of the corridor past his office and past the shower room, he could see the black hands of Dandy Crum rubbing oil into his old legs on the whiteness of the training table. He eased down the hall and identified the voice of Dee Wilkins. The two of them, the old man and the boy star, were making the private baseball talk of Negro ball-players. Barney stopped.

"I say he *goes*." Dee was saying.

"I say he *quits*," Dandy said. "I say he goes with Jeff Jones in right. After last night, he can't go with Wellington, not against this Adams. Would you? That Adams *hums* the ball. He throw *seeds*. That Adams got no respect for Wellington. Now me, he got respect, 'cause I still command it. Can he throw past me? Yeah, he can throw past me—once. Twice he hums me, man, I'm old, I know I'm old, but he better not hum me twice like I'm some scared kid he can *impress*. He got a curve ball. Let him impress me with his curve ball. He show me Big Charley. Let him come again with Big Charley, I impress him."

"I like to bunt on him," Dee said. "He crossfire me, I bunt him down first base for a hit."

"This Adams, you bunt him, bunt him down the third-base line, make him work that weak knee, throw his weight on it. If I got your speed, my bat, I do nothin' but bunt him down the third-base line. Some day, I hope Ol' Massa, I hope he call me, like last night, all he needs is a bunt down the line, I hope he call me. He think of me for the long ball, which I got in my bat, but sometime I hope he call me when all he need is a little bunt down the line."

"Here's Ol' Massa now," Barney said, interested

that word of Adams' seventh-inning knee had got around the baseball world since the trade. On the Blue Jays, not more than two or three of his closest friends had known that Jerry's knee gave him trouble toward the end of a hard game when he had to keep on throwing hard.

"Morning, Skip," Dandy said.

Barney looked at Dee sharply. "What did you have for breakfast, Dee?" In Dee's eyes he could see that Dee had been out late. "You go have Hurry get you a couple of cheeseburgers and a glass of milk. I need you all the way today."

"Yes, sir." Dee, already in uniform, ambled down the corridor.

Barney sat down on the rubbing bench beside Dandy. "What do we do to make a hitter out of Wellington?"

"You gave him the ball, Skip, you tell him you're my left fielder. It's all up to him now."

"I can't hit for him."

Dandy was rubbing his legs with the oil of warmth. "In colored ball, we played good ball, we played our jobs, but up here there is all kinds of things there wasn't there about winning. He's got to find out the *fun* of winning. Was I Wellington at his age, I come up and you give me the ball and say I'm your left fielder, I say, man, this my chance to *show* these cats. That's all I want. I hit a ball to the corner, I

run to third base first, make it back to home, just to
get to first for a single on a triple, to show them cats
they don't know the game like I know the game.
Like I used to for the Colored House of David, with
beards, in country ball. But Wellington, he comes
up, not like me, he comes up with a idea he not to
take a back seat on the diamond or off the diamond.
He want to *show* them. Man, it eats him, he want
to show them. But he don't see the fun of showing
them. He's too serious. He's so serious, he can't swing
that bat. You got to make him know it he's your left
fielder. Make him *know* it, he'll *be* your left fielder."

"Be ready to go about the seventh inning today,
Dandy," Barney said, easing off the bench. "I got an
idea I'll need you,"

"I'm ready now, I'll be ready then, you call on
me, Skip."

Barney went into his office with the strange feeling
of aloneness he had known as a player when he took
his position at shortstop—alone in his patch to defend, in view of the multitude and one with his teammates, but alone.

His office was like the commander's quarters of a
small fighting ship—compact, functional, and exclu-
sive. It was furnished with a desk and a leather
swivel chair, a straight chair for players summoned
for discipline or advice, and a leather couch for his
weary bones. An air-conditioner had been installed

in the high, small single window. There was an adjoining glass-enclosed shower and toilet, and a closet for his uniforms and clothing. The walls were undecorated. It had been the office of sixteen previous managers of the Blue Jays during the last forty years, and there was no visual evidence of any of them. When Barney left, there would be no evidence of his command.

No. 7 had been his number for twenty years as a major-leaguer and was his to keep for as long as he could keep it. As he stripped himself of his other-world clothing and became No. 7, he reduced the problem of winning today's game to the problem of destroying Jerry Adams before Jerry Adams destroyed him. He began to think of his line-up in the light of this simplicity. To hell with the Old Liners and the kids, to hell with black or white, to hell with anybody's feelings; the way to walk off the field winners was to choose the right nine guys and play them in the right order and have them do the right things to destroy Jerry Adams.

It was ten-thirty. He had to get set on his line-up in the next half-hour so the players could fit themselves into the day's pregame schedule. Baseball is a game of rigid routine that begins a hundred and fifty minutes before game time. At eleven o'clock his pitchers (except Baxley, his starter) would go to the cage for batting practice. At eleven-twenty his extra players (all except the starting line-up and one or two regular pinch-hitters) would take the cage. For forty minutes, from eleven-forty until twelve-twenty his starting line-up would take batting practice. Then the cage and field would belong to Briscoe and the Warriors for forty minutes until one o'clock. From one to one-ten the Blue Jays would have infield practice, with the Warriors following from one-ten to one-twenty. The last ten minutes before game time belonged to the groundskeeper and his crew—sprinkling, dragging, and raking the infield and marking the batter's box with fresh lime.

Jerry would be coming out contemptuous of Barney's righthanded batters and confident he could pitch carefully enough to the lefthanded power to stay out of trouble. He was expecting in the first inning to face Brooks, Wade, and Wellington. If one of them accidentally got on base, he would be pitching to Big Don Norman with two out. Why not let Jerry look at Big Don as the first man up? The object was to destroy Jerry Adams early; maybe there was a way to get him out of there before he got wet under the arms.

As he began to turn an idea and shape it into a line-up, he dialed the weather bureau number and asked for his forecaster. "What's the barometer doing, Freddy?"

"Thirty-one point two and steady."

Baseball is played with a ball that is thrown and batted through the air, spinning as it goes. The flight of a baseball is straighter and the ball is more buoyant in moist, light, thin air than it is in dry, heavy, thick air. While baseball players and tacticians accept this as an obvious truth, almost to a man (as with most other people), they think of dry, heavy, thick air as being light and lifting because it is comfortable to breathe and play in, and they think of moist, light, thin air as being heavy and oppressive because the sweat runs freely. The ball goes spinning as it is hit or thrown into the air as it is, not as it seems to be to the thinking, feeling men who hit and throw it.

Barney had had the good luck during the war to be buddies with an intellectual GI who was in weather. For two weeks in a replacement depot in North Africa, this GI had explained the aerodynamics of baseball to the first major-league ballplayer he had had a chance to unload his information and theories upon. Since then Barney had observed and tested the effects of air on baseball situations, and he now regarded aerodynamics as his own secret percentage. He did not discuss his theories and practices, and his players were unaware that many of his instructions to them and his positioning of them were based upon information he got before each game from the local weather bureaus. He was pleased to be thought of as an intuitive wizard.

"That's real good," he said. The unusually high barometer reading was a measure of unusually dry, heavy, thick air for a summer day. It was a good day for a curve-ball pitcher (like Baxley), not so good for a fast-ball pitcher (like Adams). A fly ball would have to fight the heavy air and would come down dying; he would play his outfielders in several steps closer than on a day of light air. "Wind direction and speed?"

"Northwest and a steady ten miles an hour."

The heavy air would be moving diagonally in and across the field from the left-field corner toward the right-field corner. It would tend to depress balls hit to left field and move them toward center; a well-hit ball to right would get a nice boost, but a sharply pulled ball down the right-field line would probably drift foul. Even one of Big Don's best shots to center would most likely be a long out, as one was last night.

"And temperature?"—which was least important.

"Right now it's seventy-nine degrees, and we expect it to go into the mid-eighties by early afternoon and up to ninety by late afternoon. A perfect baseball day, Barney."

"Thanks, Freddy." You don't know how perfect it

is for me, he thought as he put the phone down and looked at one of the printed scorecards that were being sold to the fans for today's game.

With a smile of mirth and malice he looked at the probable starting line-up he had given Tom Poole, their publicity man, to give to the printers before last night's defeat. It showed:

Brooks, 2B
Wade, ss
Wellington, LF
Norman, 1B
T. Jones, RF
Tuffson, 3B
Wilkins, CF
Slater, c
Baxley, P

His long nose twitched in excitement as he crossed out every name except Baxley's and inserted the following:

Norman, 1B
Sandowski, 3B
Crum, LF
Slater, c
Brooks, 2B
Wilkins, CF
Wellington, RF
Wade, ss

It was a beautifully radical line-up; it made him excited and confident to look at it. He smiled again as he thought of the commotion and rhubarb-rhubarb-rhubarb from the stands as the fans scrambled with their pencils to keep up with the field announcer's professional chant. He smiled a third time as he thought of the excitement and consternation in the voice of Andy Water, the radio announcer, as he reported and tried to comment on the desperation of Barney Mann.

"He's got Norman, the league's batting champion and leader in home runs and runs batted in, hitting *first*. He's got Sandowski, one of the slowest men on the team, hitting second, and Old Dandy Crum, the veteran outfielder, who lost his speed five years ago and who's only hitting one ninety-two this year, batting third. In the cleanup spot he's got Slater, the catcher, who's even slower than Sandowski and hasn't hit a home run all year. Then he follows with Brooks, Wilkins, and Wellington, his three fastest base runners, and in eighth place is Wade, who's hitting three thirty-one and who leads the league in doubles and is second only to Norman in runs batted in. Folks, I don't know . . . I've never seen anything . . . Listen to the crowd as they follow Charley Smith, the field announcer. . . ."

He entered his radical line-up on the regular line-up card, which was a packet containing two carbons, so that it was in triplicate. This was the same form he would fill in and bring to his meeting with the umpires and Briscoe just before game time. Hurry would post this one for his own people—one copy on the clubhouse wall next to the street entrance, so the players could see it as they came in, and a second copy on the door to the dugout, so there would be no mistake about who was to take regular hitting practice.

The trouble with the normal procedure was that many of the opposing players went through the home-team dugout and across the field to their own, and they would have a chance to see his radical starting line-up before game time. Adams would have a chance to think; Briscoe would have a chance to think; they would get together and talk over how they were going to pitch to four tough left-handers leading off. Briscoe might even change starting pitchers on him and come up with that old Dipsy Doodle McDonald, the curve-ball lefthander who had made a career out of getting lefthanded hitters out in key spots; then he could put Adams in after an inning or two. Briscoe and Adams must not know of his starting line-up until game time. The way to keep a secret was to keep it to yourself.

But if he assigned his new starting line-up to regular batting practice, he might just as well post the

line-up, because the Warriors would be watching
to see who came up to hit. He tore the card up and
let the pieces fall like confetti into the wastebasket.
On a fresh card he wrote heavily: "Following will
take batting practice—Brooks, Sandowski, Tuffson,
Cruise, Slater, Crum, Wade, Wellington, Norman,
T. Jones, J. Jones, Wilkins. Clubhouse meeting after
regular batting practice for everybody."

He looked at it and smiled. Now his radical line-
up was perfectly camouflaged by the kind of schedule a losing manager, deep in a losing streak, following an extra-inning night game, might come up with
on Sunday. Briscoe would figure he did not want
his regulars, tired after a late night game, to spend as
much time in the hitting cage as usual, so he had
spread batting practice among the pinch-hitters and
substitutes. He smiled again and tapped the buzzer
to signal for Hurry.

"Yes, Barney."

"Post this and ask Wellington to come in when he
gets suited up."

Hurry closed the door, and Barney picked up the
phone and dialed Mike's office upstairs in the main
office. Normally Barney did not consult the general
manager about line-ups and game tactics. But this
was not normal. There was no answer, and he dialed
Olga Wendt, the switchboard operator.

"Hello, Olga. Have you heard from our beloved general manager yet this morning?"

"Hasn't come in yet, Barney. But Young Dud just came in." Young Dud and his sister Lissie had inherited the ball club from their father, Old Dud, dead these fifteen years. "I think he's coming down to see you."

"Maybe I'd better hide. Okay, Olga, thanks."

Young Dud left the operation of the club entirely to Mike. Or he had up to now. Maybe he was coming to fire Barney; maybe to ask him to autograph a ball for a grandson's playmate.

Barney dialed Mike's home number and caught him just as he was leaving the house. "Mike, I'm going to try a new line-up today. It's like nothing you ever saw, and I want you to know about it before anybody else. Nobody else is going to know about it until the clubhouse meeting."

"Go ahead."

Barney gave it to him.

"Why?" Mike asked, his voice as heavy and dry as the day's air.

"I've got to get Adams out of there early. If he goes even seven innings, Briscoe will come with old Dipsy Doodle McDonald, and I won't get the five or six runs I'll need to win this one. I want Adams and Briscoe to like to drop dead when I lead off with Norman and follow with my best lefthanded strength. Then I come at him with my speed kids, and they're going to bunt and run him dizzy. Besides, once the innings begin to roll, who can tell what part of the line-up is coming up anyway? Once we get rolling, my speed kids will be coming up ahead of my power. That's why I've got Wade hitting eighth behind them. By having Norman lead off, I'll probably get an extra at-bat out of him. And one extra at-bat out of Norman can be a ball game." He had the feeling that he was not telling it right. Maybe he should have gone ahead without checking it out with Mike.

"It's your show, Barney, you know that."

"You don't like it."

"I would not say it is my line-up. I would say that I think it is a hell of a day to gamble and experiment."

"Gamble? That means taking your best chance. Experiment? There isn't a man in that line-up that I don't know what he can do in a given situation."

"You're going with Wellington against Adams?"

"He hit Adams good last year."

"Last year."

"I've got to go this way, Mike."

"It's your show, Barney. Good luck."

Still my show. Why fight it? All he had to do was

bench Wellington and go back to a conventional line-up and leave the winning or the losing of the game to the men on the field. "Thanks, Mike."

There was a tap on the door, and it was Wellington.

He came in, competent and unconfident, scared and unafraid. What had Paulson said? "We see ourselves in our heroes." Barney saw himself in Wellington.

"Sit down, Bill, and stretch your legs. Are you and your family getting settled?"

"We've got an apartment, not where we want to be. We're looking for a house, but I guess we won't find anybody to sell us one in any neighborhood we want to live in."

"Things are changing, Bill. We've come a long way since Jackie Robinson. Do you go to church, Bill?"

"My wife and kids go, but the church we're going to, it's only got one service on Sunday, and that would bring me here too late for batting practice."

"If you had asked me, I would have excused you from batting practice today, Bill."

"Because you're not starting me today anyway," Bill said.

"I'm not starting you today in left field, Bill," Barney said. He lit a cigar and leaned way back in his chair and put his spikes on his desk. "I'm starting you in right today. The wind is strong toward right, and I'm starting Crum in left, which means Wilkins will have to take more of left center, which means you will have to play toward center and still get to the line. You got the speed to do it."

"You're giving me another chance?"

"I gave up too much to get you to give up on you, Bill."

"I haven't been playing good ball for you, Skipper, and last night—I've got no excuses for last night."

Barney nodded and sucked at his cigar and blew the smoke out in little puffs without inhaling. "I didn't sleep too good last night, either. One of the things I thought about was you and me, Bill. How we both had the same troubles. When I came up with the Blue Jays, it was in nineteen forty-two, the year before I went into the Army, and I couldn't hit the broad side of a barn door. I couldn't hit nothing—not lefthanders, righthanders, fast balls, or curves. I went zero for fourteen before I got a scratch single. Old Mr. Dudley was manager in those days, and one Sunday, a day pretty much like today—we were trying to battle out of a losing streak and stay in contention—Old Dud called me into this very office, like I've called you in, and he gave me this." From his drawer Barney, leaning forward, fished out a coin. "And Old Dud said, 'Barney, you're still my shortstop, but you've got to help me prove it. Now take this quarter and go out there and give me at

least two bits' worth today.' That day I got a double
and a single, they walked me once, and I flied deep
to center for an RBI. So I say the same to you. Take
this quarter and go out there and give me two bits'
worth today, and you keep this quarter until some
day, some kid will need it as bad as I needed it then
and you need it now."

Bill opened his hand, and Barney put the coin into
it. Bill closed his hand and lowered his head. Barney
could not see his eyes.

"Maybe it won't work for you, Bill," Barney said.
"You're not superstitious like me. You've got a good
education and all. I know a lot about Jerry Adams,
how he works and how he thinks. I may give you
some take signs when you don't expect them, and be
ready to bunt at any time, even with two strikes."

Bill was clutching the coin. Now he raised his
head. "I didn't hear all you said, Skip. Tell me that
again."

Barney told him again.

"I'll give you two bits' worth today, Skip."

When Bill had left, Barney sat back and sucked
his cigar, thinking that maybe he should have made
Wellington laugh instead of cry. But tears are tears,
and tears clean the eyes. In baseball, you can't hit
what you can't see.

It wasn't even eleven o'clock, and he had his line-
up made up and most of his thinking done. Suddenly

he wanted to go out and shag fly balls. He felt a yearning to get a line on a fly ball and shag after it and be there to bring it in. As an infielder, he had always enjoyed throwing knuckle balls and shagging fly balls more than picking up grounders. Now he wanted to shag, to be a player sweating free in the morning sunshine.

He walked into the clubhouse to show his people that he and they were going out there to play a ball game that he knew how to win. None of his stars and few of his regulars, except Wellington and Wilkins, had showed yet, which was okay for a Sunday after an extra-inning night game, and the middle of the locker row was unoccupied, but there were clusters of players at both ends. Barney wondered if he had done right in assigning Wellington a middle locker before he had earned it in his new uniform.

"Let's see your hand," he said to Zen Murdock, a young pitcher with a strong arm and bad judgment. Zen had flagged down a line drive with his meat hand the week before. The index finger was still swollen at the knuckle. Zen squeezed. "I got a good grip on the ball," Zen said. "I'm ready to go."

"Barney! See you a moment?"

It was Johnston Dudley, Young Dud, the playboy of the western division. He lived the simple bird life of the warblers—to Rainy Lake in Ontario in the summer and to the Virgin Islands in the winter. Unlike the warblers, he and his sister Lissie, who lived off the income of the ball club and other properties Old Dud had bequeathed them, migrated conspicuously and with bright-plumed celebrities in current vogue. He is going to tell me that this losing streak is bad for his best interests, so why don't I solve his problems and mine by ending it, Barney thought, feeling a flush of anger and cool all over.

"Mr. Dudley," he said, extending his hand, "some of these boys haven't had a chance to meet you. Here's Zen Murdock, who has got a better chance of winning twenty games than any other young meathead in baseball. And Dave Messengale, who's after Big Don Norman's job." He took him up and down the line and then into his office, where he jockeyed him into the straight chair while he sat in his own and leaned back and looked at him over the toes of his spikes on the desk.

"I like your humor, Barney. I hope you can win us a pennant. Anything I can do?"

"No, sir. There's nothing you or Mike can get for me. We're a set club, and we're running for all the money."

"That isn't what I came for." He was an attractive old young man—lean, weathered, and sprightly. "Lissie's in town with me, on her way from New York to the Coast with some theatrical and television people. I want you to round up half a dozen of your boys and come to a party I'm giving at my home tonight."

"Wives?" Barney asked.

"No wives."

"Mike?"

"Mike doesn't like to be with drinking people."

"Who do you want?"

"This is mostly the Jimmy James group."

"Will he be there?" Barney had never met the funny man with the legendary capacity for booze and women.

"His complete entourage. Five or six girls."

"Who do you want to come?"

"You. There's a female writer, a very wild woman, wants to meet you. And Norman, of course. And Wade. And your Negro fellas—Crum and Jones for laughs. Wilkins and Wellington."

"Not Wellington. Wilkins maybe, not Wellington. He's not a party man."

"A friend of mine, a divorced lady, has a thing about colored men. She has been suffering with Wellington. Wants to mother him out of his slump."

"Mother what him?"

"You're funny, but I mean it."

"Their time is their own when they walk off that field. I'll ask. But I got to square it with Mike, Mr. Dudley. He knows what I know."

"Just don't ask him to the party. Tell him from me he is not invited."

"You tell him that, Mr. Dudley."

"When will you know who's coming?"

"You gonna be in the owner's box?" The owner's box was at the side of the dugout. "Just before game time, when they're dragging the infield, I should know."

"About five o'clock, right from the park."

Five o'clock seemed as remote as heaven or hell.

"Come a winner, and we'll have more fun. And call me Johnse tonight."

"Yes, sir." He walked Johnse to the clubhouse door and turned around to find Dave Messengale, a red-headed boy, only twenty, a kid from Scranton, a first baseman, his understudy to Big Don Norman, wanting to talk. "Going out?" Barney asked him.

They left the clubhouse and walked the screened-in bridge over the concession booths under the stands where the fans stood to catch a glimpse and to call a word of cheer or derision to their heroes. There were already a lot of fans milling around, mostly waiting to get their beer and hot dogs for batting-practice sustenance. Dave said, "Skip, could I ask you something?"

"You want to go back to Omaha and play regular," Barney told him.

"I don't feel I'm bettering myself riding the bench and doing a little pinch-hitting and -running. I've only been to bat six times."

"I know, Dave."

"I got two hits."

"I need you, Dave, I'm gonna need you more come July, when the infield gets hard under Big Don's legs. You're gonna play the second game of double-headers, and we already got four games to make up, plus the ones we got scheduled. You'll play."

"I feel I can hit Adams. I've seen him. I think I could pull his curve and meet his fast ball." The kid wanted to play today. They were in the dank concrete room just inside the dugout, where there were a water fountain, a toilet, and the bats of the extra players. Barney stopped and looked at him, as if for the first time. The boy had a thatch of red hair and dark brown eyes and a baby face with soft red fuzz on his chin. And yet he had a hawklike meanness about him, poised and restless. He was a skinny kid—six-one and a hundred and seventy, supple, loose, and very quick. He threw and hit lefthanded. He wanted to play. He wanted to play in Big Don's place today.

"You know Al Hemminger, with Tulsa last year?" the boy said. "He throws as hard as Adams and keeps it down. I hit him good last year."

"His fast ball. But where's his curve, screwball, forkball, and change?"

"I don't mean he's an Adams."

"You'll probably get a shot today." Barney put his

hand on the kid's shoulder. "You're learning more up here than you know you're learning."

On the field was the orderly chaos of pregame practice. Nordstrom, the batting-practice pitcher, was throwing to the pitchers, who were being watched by both Bill Tate, the pitching coach, and Jinx Moore, the batting coach. Granny Wolf was hitting fungos to the extras.

There were already four or five thousand fans scattered in the stands and in the sunshine of the bleachers, loving the game so much they wanted to be a part of every part of it. Barney wondered if people had come early to the Greek theaters Paulson was talking about to watch acting practice. Feeling as tense and wary as if he were stepping out of the dugout to pick out a bat and go to the plate against Jerry Adams with a man on second and two out, he eased himself to his height and walked slowly, kicking at dirt clods along the way, down the third-base line to where Granny was knocking out fungos. He and Granny had made more double plays in their time together than any other shortstop–second baseman in the history of the game—without any affection between them. They had showed each other the ball—and nothing else.

"Whattaya say, Gran?"

"He's gonna be rough today, Barney. This wind is gonna help his crossfire against our righties."

This heavy air is gonna take something off his fast ball, Barney said silently.

Granny walloped a ball to right center, and Barney watched its flight critically. Wilkins took an automatic step back and then came in fast as the ball drifted and died in the heavy moving air.

"Send him back for one," Barney said.

Granny, who could drop a fungo into a bucket in any part of the field, gave a ball a long ride to deep center. Dee loafed back and pounded his glove waiting for it. "Some balls are deader than others," Granny said, taking a toss from Len Michaels, the young third catcher. He hit a long skyscraper that drifted to right center. Dee speared it against the wall.

"Tough wind field out there," Michaels remarked.

"What kind of meeting did you call?" Granny asked.

"How we're gonna play Adams."

"You got a line-up?" Granny's eyes were deep-set and a cold blue-white under his black brows.

"I'm gonna try something we haven't tried before," Barney said and went down the line, kicking at clods, toward the batting cage, feeling Granny's cold eyes in his back.

"Give everybody extra bunting today, Jinx," he said to his old mate, the center fielder on the last championship team. Jinx also was first-base coach, and the best sign-stealer in the league.

Barney moved next to Bill Tate, his pitching coach. "Who is our long man if Baxley gets bombed early?"

"Cruise is ready, and the work wouldn't hurt Anderson none." They were both righthanders. Cruise was a calm, steady workman who could throw strikes; his trouble was he threw too many of them; but he made you beat him. Anderson was the fifth starter, who hadn't had much his last time out but might have everything today; he was a smart pitcher with a good down-breaking curve ball, which figured to break even more sharply in today's heavy air.

"How about Kunz?" Barney asked. "His knuckle ball would be a zombie in this air."

"They're all ready," Tate said. "Whoever we need at the time."

"Murdock tells me he can grip the ball good and throw hard."

Tate agreed. "He was really firing the ball for me yesterday. But I wouldn't want to use him in a spot where he could hit a batter or walk us into trouble."

Mel, the batboy, came trotting alongside. "Sir, you're wanted on the dugout phone."

It was Tom Poole, their publicity man. "Are you coming up pretty soon, Barney? They're all here."

"Who's all here?"

"Those visiting foreign professors and philosophers."

Three weeks ago, in the world of first place, he had promised Tom, with a lighthearted joke, that he would meet with these foreign intellectuals the State Department was carting around the country and tell them about the great American game.

"I can't do it today, Tom."

"They've been around the country looking at factories, universities, art museums, slums, mansions. Today is sports day for them. What makes baseball the great American game? And you are it, Barney."

"When I told you I'd do it today, I didn't know about today."

"It's a State Department deal. Senator Short is here with them. They're up in the boardroom right now. We're having lunch brought in for them. You don't want them to go home hating America more than they do now, do you?"

"I've got a clubhouse meeting."

"Please give these people half an hour between now and then, Barney. You promised."

He put the phone down and walked slowly up the gloomy passageway until he came to the enclosed bridge over the fans milling around the concession stands. He walked briskly across the bridge and into the clubhouse like a man who knew what he was doing.

3

Barney walked into the boardroom of oak and leather in his stocking feet. A bar had been set up at the far end. Fifteen men, wearing their middle age and sports coats well, were standing in clusters, drinking sherry or beer. They seemed robust and jovial. Barney had the feeling that he had walked into the barroom of a rich man's shooting club instead of a den of sparring intellectuals. He spotted only one short-nosed egghead. The rest of them had noses—long, fat, thin, straight, and crooked, but noses. Baseball players, come to think of it, ran more to chin than to nose.

Senator Short spotted him first. "Wonderful to see you again, Barney. Wonderful of you to give these folks your time today."

"How are you, sir?"

"Excuse me, Senator. Barney, this is Dr. Berenson of the International Behavioral Science Council," Tom Poole said, propelling a bald little man with bright blue eyes past the senator. "He's in charge of the group and will act as interpreter."

Barney took the small hand. "I'm supposed to tell them about a game they don't know in a language they don't understand?"

"They all have English, but they may need some help with idiom."

"You mean idiot?"

"I'm a baseball fan myself, Barney—and a particular fan of yours."

"I don't know how hard the infield is, Doctor. What am I supposed to do?"

"There's an example," Dr. Berenson said. "How would you translate 'how hard the infield is' into French and Russian?"

"I'm not supposed to tell them how to play ball, am I?"

"We chose you—I did, I might say—because you are one of the most articulate and socially aware men in baseball. You stay right here at this end of the table. I'll get them seated and introduce you to them and them to you. This will not be a colloquium, but simply an informal conversation about baseball and professional sports as one of the cultural themes of American life."

"Who are they?"

"Mostly behavioral scientists, academic people."

Barney looked steadily down into his eyes.

"Social scientists, psychologists, an anthropologist . . . Two of them are psychiatrists, and we have two novelists, a Frenchman and a Russian. The Swede is a physiological psychologist, and the Indian is a biochemical psychologist. So you can see we have a well-rounded group."

"What do they want to know?"

"They're preparing an overview of the operating characteristics of the American system—its formal organization, its myth-making, its combination of rigidity and fluidity, caution and daring, and its informal adjustive controls. Their analysis has ranged from poverty and poor living conditions to politics and propaganda, and they are now examining the divertissements supplied by the popular arts and entertainment forms."

"Let's get going," Barney said. "I've got a ball game to get ready for."

"Gentlemen! Gentlemen!" Dr. Berenson called and went to get them seated.

Tom Poole raised his glass of beer. "I'm sorry, Barney."

Senator Short was standing by. "The impressions that these folks get of America can be of importance for many years to come, Barney," he said, nodding as if in agreement with his own wisdom. "It may take a while to percolate down to their governments and peoples, but the work and thought of intellectuals have a broad and continuing impact on every country, including our own."

"Impact," Barney said. "I ought to give my guys a broad and continuing impact on their asses."

"I'll sit right here beside you and help in any way I can."

"I'll try to keep it clean, Senator," Barney said.

They were all seated now, except Dr. Berenson at his end of the table, and Barney at his. Dr. Berenson addressed them. "It is our pleasure this morning, before playing our role as spectators at an American professional baseball game, to have a chance to interview Mr. Barney Mann, manager of the Blue Jays, one of the oldest and most successful teams, year in and year out, in the National League."

The brief applause was interrupted by the applauders, who, with Dr. Berenson and each other, raised questions in up to three languages. Finally the questions were answered, and all heads nodded in solemn agreement.

"We were discussing the significance of 'National' and 'American' as applied to the two major leagues, Barney," Dr. Berenson explained. "There was a question as to whether they were equivalent, or merely comparable, with 'Republican' and 'Democratic' as the formal designations of our two principal political parties."

"What did they decide?" Barney asked.

"That they were comparable, but without significant equivalency. Now, Barney, going around the table from Senator Short, I would like to introduce these gentlemen to you."

Each of them smiled and bobbed his head and raised his glass to Barney, who tried to concentrate on where they were from instead of on their meaningless names. Most of them were from universities—Moscow, West Berlin, Uppsala, Heidelberg, Chicago, Padua, Allahabad, Sorbonne, California at Los Angeles, Leningrad. . . . Leningrad, who had the longest and most drooping nose of them all, was at Barney's left.

Barney fixed each with a steady eye and nodded in personal recognition.

"Gentlemen," he began, but was immediately interrupted by the jabber-buzz of several tongues.

Dr. Berenson listened and talked until there was again a general nodding of heads.

"Barney, they want to know something about your job. How much you are paid and what your security is."

"My salary is confidential between me and my club. Tell them I am well paid and live in a high-rent neighborhood. As for security, I have a contract that runs through this season. If they fire me before the season is over, they have to pay me for the whole season."

"Winning, I think it is, winning depends your job?" This was from Moscow.

"I am expected to get the best from the personnel acquired by the front office. If the front office has players it thinks can win, it expects me to win with them. If I can't get the job done, it gives the opportunity to someone else. I don't see that it's much different from any other kind of a job in a competitive situation."

"It seems to me that it is much different," said the anthropologist from the University of Chicago. He was a slim old man with a deeply lined face and strong, nervous hands. "In business, in government, and in education and research, success is often ambiguous. We often do not know ourselves whether we are succeeding or failing. Further, we can conceal our mistakes and losses from others, sometimes even from ourselves. We keep mediocre and even bad people around because we do not have the necessity or courage to get rid of them. A wasted day, a sloppy performance, a bad decision—who knows? And who cares? But in baseball there is no ambiguity. The score and the complete record of the game are recorded instantly and permanently. There is no way to conceal a flaw or hide a mistake from the multitude of knowledgeable and observant critics, who discuss and debate every tactic and action."

"We charge admission," Barney remarked, "so they've got a right to see what goes on and to complain if they don't like it."

"Perhaps," suggested a dark-haired man who sounded Swedish, "we should put numbers on the backs of our representatives in government, on our factory workers, and on our scientists, and charge admission to the parliament, the factory, and the laboratory."

His friend, who was blond and sounded Italian, broke in with laughter. "But of course! The people should not pay taxes to support us, they should pay admission to see us work, as in this game of baseball."

"Throw the bum out!" cried Dr. Berenson happily.

"But Barney," said old Chicago U., "you said your responsibility was to get the best out of the players assigned to you."

"Yes, sir."

"But don't you also have a good deal of responsibility for the selection of your players? It has been widely reported that the recent trade of Adams for Wellington was *your* trade."

"That's right, it was. The front office listens to

my recommendations." Barney grinned at him. "You sound like a fan."

"Since I was a boy on Coogan's Bluff," he said with pride.

"What do *you* think of the trade?" Barney asked him.

"I like it for the future. I don't think you would have been able to get Wellington for Adams next year. But I think there is merit to the argument that you may have weakened your chances for the pennant this year," the other answered with scholarly firmness.

"So far you look good."

"Perhaps we will have better insight after today's game?"

"Maybe." Barney nodded. "If there are no other questions, I'd better be—"

"Your strategy and tactics on the field," said slouchy young Dr. Southern California, who spoke from between the fingers with which he was holding up his loose chin, "are mainly showmanship, aren't they? I mean the fetish and rigmarole of such maneuvers as the hit-and-run, the sacrifice, taking one pitcher out and putting in another, and so on— actually all that is more showmanship than meaningful strategy, isn't it?"

"Those are things you do to increase your chances

of winning," Barney said politely. "I wouldn't say we do it to put on an act. Baseball is a game of percentages. In any situation, one type of play or using a particular player will give you a better chance of success than another play with some other player. What you do in a given situation depends on the abilities of the players you have available and those playing against you. For example, suppose you have men in scoring position and you need a base hit to get them home, and the righthanded batter coming up has not had good success against the righthanded pitcher he is facing. You figure you've got a better chance of getting the runs home if you come in with a lefthanded batter. But you also have got to figure that in doing so you may be weakening yourself defensively by taking the regular batter out of the lineup. Another thing you think about is that the opposing manager may take his righthanded pitcher out of the game and put in a lefthander who has had good success against your pinch-hitter. If he does that, you may have to come up with a good righthanded batter to hit against *him*. Those are just some of the things you think about in a situation like that."

"You have much information—the records of the different players—available to you?"

Dr. Berenson beamingly interjected, "There is probably no form of competitive human endeavor on which there are such complete data as baseball."

"That may be right," Barney said. "And what isn't on paper is in your head. After all, counting spring training, exhibition, and World Series, and your own one hundred and sixty-two games a season, the average manager sees something like two hundred games a year. You do that for twenty-five years, and you ought to learn something about the game and the people who play it."

"With all the data available, it would seem to me that a manager could be replaced by a computer in the dugout," said Dr. Southern California. "You could give the computer all the data on all the alternatives and let it work out your problem."

"I don't doubt that the day will come when we eggheads will take over in the dugout too," Dr. Berenson said cheerfully.

"Meanwhile," Barney said, "I've got to figure out my line-up to start against Adams today, so if there are no more . . ."

"I presume you will get as many lefthanded batters as possible into your line-up today?" old Chicago U. asked.

"The only machine I've got," Barney said, putting a finger to his head, "hasn't finished working out the problem."

"Why is it, Barney," asked Dr. Berenson, "that a lefthanded batter has a better chance against a righthanded pitcher than against a lefthanded pitcher? And vice versa?"

"That is a fact of American life that is better known than it is understood," old Chicago U. said. "I have never understood it. When I played ball as a boy and hit righthanded, I always felt more confident and less terrified when facing a righthanded pitcher than I did against a lefthanded pitcher."

Barney nodded. "Most boys who play baseball are righthanded, and most of the pitching they see as righthanded batters is righthanded. They get accustomed to it, and the occasional lefthanded pitcher, who is probably a little wild and erratic, is strange to them. But in professional baseball there is a good balance between lefthanded and righthanded power, whether it be hitting or throwing. There is a demand for lefthanders, and a good many boys who want to become professional players develop their abilities to throw and bat lefthanded. So we see a lot of both."

"But assuming a batter gets accustomed to hitting against both right- and lefthanded pitching, why does the righthanded batter have a better chance against the lefthanded pitcher?"

"Because he can see the ball better from the time it leaves the pitcher's hand. If you will, Doctor, stand up there at your end of the table and face me as if you were a batter hitting against me." The old man got up spryly and took a creditable stance. Barney went through the motions of a pitcher and came down with his right hand and stopped at the point at which he would release the ball. "Now, you see, you are looking at my hand out of the corners of your eyes from over your shoulder. The ball will come diagonally in toward you on its way to the plate. You may have to give ground, back away from the plate, to keep from getting hit, until at the last split second you see that the ball is going to be over the plate. That's for a fast ball. But now suppose I come in on you with my curve. The ball will come toward you all the way, breaking suddenly out away from you and over the plate. But you can't wait to start your swing until you can see where the ball is going to be. You have got to start your swing within a split second after the ball is thrown and adjust your swing to meet the ball. Now, let's suppose I am pitching lefthanded against you." Barney made a wind-up motion and came down lefthanded. "Now you can see the ball as it leaves my hand more directly. The ball comes from the outside in toward you and the plate. Furthermore, my curve now starts wide and then breaks in to the plate. You can see the ball better all the way, and you can get more firmly set against the pitcher."

"Yes, of course," said old Chicago U., taking a good cut at the imaginary curve.

"We do not come to talk techniques, but ideas," Moscow said.

"That's true," said Dr. Berenson. "It is not essential to the enjoyment of the game to understand its fine points. After all, the bumpkin may enjoy an opera without understanding that a key which is comfortable and ensures the full power of one singer may be uncomfortable and restricting to his partner in a duet." To Moscow: "Did you have a question or comment?"

"In American professional sports, winning is everything."

"Winning is not everything," Barney told him. "It is the only thing."

This was followed by a cross-examination of Dr. Berenson and one another as to the significance of his statement. Tablets had appeared in front of most of them, and they were taking notes.

"What they want to get at, Barney," Dr. Berenson said when the heads were nodding instead of shaking, "is whether the emphasis is on winning or on the welfare of the individual player."

"We build character by trying to produce winners," Barney told them. "We don't think that losing is good for the player or the club."

"But there are losers, of course," the Englishman said.

"That's right."

"What is their reward?"

"Baseball is a hard game for hard men," Barney said slowly. "Played with undivided interest, it is a satisfying outlet for rugged men who like physical effort. Premiums are paid for strenuous effort and for the subordination of self-interest for the good of the team. Played halfheartedly, baseball is a waste of time and energy. Baseball is not a halfway game. Players and managers who take it easy on the field come to grief and failure. To play baseball, you have to get wet all over."

There was much discussion of these remarks, and Barney got the notion he could pad out in his stocking feet and they never would know that he had padded out.

"This is very good, Barney," the senator said.

"Very good," Tom Poole echoed. "I mean it. I wish we had asked some of the sportswriters in."

"They are relating what you have told them to the competitive nature of the capitalistic system," Dr. Berenson said beamingly.

"Gentlemen," Barney said. "I've got a lot to do on the field and in the clubhouse before today's game."

"Winning is not everything," Moscow said. "It is the only thing."

"Yes," Barney said. "And, gentlemen, I have a game to try to win today. If I may, before I get back to it, I will tell you about a talk I had with a sportswriter this morning. This man said that baseball is to Americans what the theater was to the Greeks in olden days. He said the Greeks came out to see their heroes and gods suffer and sweat in situations familiar to everybody. He said that Americans feel the same way about baseball. They know the players and they know the game, so they come out to see how the players respond to the challenges of a particular game. But I think he was wrong about one thing. The difference between the Greek theater and American professional baseball is that they played with heroes, and we play with people. I know my players, but I am not sure what they will do, or can do in any game. Baseball is a game that boys play for fun and men play for keeps. Baseball is our living. Our living is a baseball game that we must try to win. There are no tie games in baseball, and there is only one winner."

Some of them were writing, to take down every word, and some of them were listening, to hear every word. Barney smiled. "Thank you, gentlemen," he said. "I gotta get back to my club."

As he closed the door, the applause was interrupted again by the excited jabber-buzz of foreign tongues trying to make something complicated out of the simple facts of life.

4

He sat solitary in his dugout, looking out at his field and his players. It was ten minutes after twelve, and his regulars were taking batting practice. His clubhouse meeting would begin as soon after twelve-twenty as his players and coaches could assemble. He would be alone with them to show them a way to win.

Is it my game to win, Barney asked himself, or is it their game to win?

He looked out at his field and players and saw, without watching the stances and swings of his batters, the flight of each driven ball, and the movements of the fielders as they trotted or ran to be at the end of each flight and bounce. He saw as a musician hears. Seeing without watching, he looked into his clear question.

But Tom Poole's shadow was there with a question of the proper order of the baseball day. "Everybody's waiting for your starting line-up."

"Everybody? Briscoe?"

"He posted his in the usual manner."

"He'll get mine when I give it to him and the umpires."

"Your own coaches and players are asking me if you've given it out yet."

"They'll get it at the clubhouse meeting."

"When do I get copies for the press box and the field announcer?"

"Jinx will give you a copy before I go out." Barney raised his head and looked at Tom steadily to send him away. Tom went away, knowing that he would be there when Barney was long gone.

Barney looked again into his own question and talked to his unwatched but seen players. "Maybe you are heroes, like the writer said. Each and all of you wants the chance to play in the game and be the one that wins it, and not one of you is afraid he'll be the one that kicks it away or lets it leak away. I sit here without a chance to win it or kick it away out there. It is up to you heroes to win it or lose it. But I say who plays and who does what, so that puts it all back on me. I manage you, and I manage it. How we play this game depends on what I do with you. How we remember this game—and nobody on this field is ever going to forget a play of it—depends on what I do with you. Right now you are just ballplayers going through the motions of the game. That is all you will be until I show you how you can play this game to win and make you believe you can win it. It is up to you to play this game, but it is up to me to win it." He lowered his head and took a final look into his question. "It is my game to win."

He got up and walked through the tunnel and over the bridge and into the clubhouse to his office. He closed the door and was alone with his game.

5

He looked at the line-up he had made out in secret over an hour before and felt the cold blue of Granny Wolf's stare in his back. He had to make use of Granny Wolf in the destruction of Jerry Adams. Granny Wolf was a destroyer. If Granny Wolf helped destroy Jerry Adams, he would destroy himself as an agent of the destruction of Barney's team. Granny Wolf was as simple as fire; he was for you or against you. "I've got to have Granny with me today," Barney said aloud. He leaned back in his chair. He did not have to count upon Granny's loyalty to the team. Granny was a baseball man; in a baseball situation, he could respond only as a baseball man.

With him in the line-up in place of Brooks, the club would be weakened even further defensively. Wolf was merely reliable at second; Brooks was reliably brilliant. Sandowski could not make any of the tough plays at third that Tuffson made look easy. Crum was an old black joke in left field. But Barney could not win without destroying Jerry Adams. Wolf,

Sandowski, and Crum, with Norman and Slater, could destroy Adams with their lefthanded power, and his three righthanded batters—Wilkins, Wellington, and Wade—could run over the pieces.

With Wolf in the line-up, he changed his batting order. He got out a triplicate of fresh line-up cards. Firmly, slowly, and finally, he printed the names. He realized that Marianna would always believe he had taken her advice.

He put the packet in his back pocket and buzzed for Hurry Harry and asked him to bring a carton of milk and a peanut-butter-and-jelly sandwich. He stretched out on his couch and relaxed until the food came. He sipped and ate slowly, knowing that his people were waiting. They had been beaten nine games in a row by ordinary opposition; now they must believe they could beat Jerry Adams.

6

They might have been oarsmen on a Viking ship at ease in their places before a fatal engagement. All were in their chairs in front of their lockers, facing the aisle and their leader. Some were in full uniform, and some were nearly naked. Some leaned back, hands clasped behind their necks; some leaned forward, elbows on their knees. There would be no need to say anything twice.

Bill Wellington was not now concerned with his inability to buy a house in a residential neighborhood appropriate to his economic status and his middle-class aspirations, or even with his failure to get the fat of the bat on the ball. He was placing himself in the team effort. Big Don Norman, the superstar, was not now concerned with his third wife's lackadaisical efforts to achieve full marital bliss, or with his dude ranch in Montana, or with his mining interests, or even with his batting average. He was placing himself in the team effort. Dave Messengale, Big Don's eager understudy, was not now concerned with playing, but with making the right moves if called upon to run or hit in a crisis. And so with all of them except Granny Wolf, who lounged easily against a far locker and stared blue cold into Barney.

Barney stood at his end of the aisle. "I didn't post the starting line-up as usual this morning, because there was no way to post it for you without posting it for Briscoe and Adams. There are some surprises in it for them. It is a line-up that will weaken us some defensively. It is designed to get Adams out of there in four or five innings. If we can do that, we will tighten up defensively and take it home from there." He walked slowly up the aisle and stopped and dropped his hand on Big Don's shoulder. "Hitting first today is Don Norman. He'll give Adams something to think about coming out, and it may give Big Don another time at bat today."

Big Don looked up and shifted his quid, made up of two parts chewing gum and one part chewing tobacco. "You ain't lookin' for me to steal second, are you, Barney?"

The players raised their heads and smiled; in smiling they became more at one with one another. The young players knew they were among giants.

"You ain't gonna have to steal second, Don, because hitting behind you is Dandy Crum." And he walked the few steps to him. "Dandy has hit three pinch homers off Adams, two when he was with the

Pirates and a grandslammer for the Cubs. Dandy, you're starting in left field."

Dandy looked up with the biggest smile in baseball. "I'm ready, Skip."

"Hitting third today is a lefthanded hitter who battles a pitcher as tough as anybody in baseball." He walked to the end of the aisle and put his hand on the shoulder of Granny Wolf. "Granny will start at second." There was a momentary glint of fire from beneath the black brows before Granny nodded impassively. Barney glanced at Brooks, who had expected to start. The boy took a deep breath and blew it out against his folded hands and nodded at his shoes. "Hitting in fourth place, starting at third base, is another of the greatest lefthanded power hitters in baseball." He walked to Sandowski.

"That's what he means by weakening us defensively," Sandowski said with his quick grin.

"I'm not worried about anything getting through you, Sandy."

"Not through me," Sandy admitted. "Past me."

"I'll make 'em hit right to you, Sandy," Baxley said, "on an easy hop."

"Hitting fifth is another dose of lefthanded power. Red Slater."

"I always figured I was a fifth-place hitter, Barney," the craggy catcher squeaked out.

"You weren't kidding, Barney," said Jinx Moore,

"you said you were going to give Adams and Briscoe a surprise. I don't know of any righthanded pitcher ever looked at more brutal lefthanded hitters in a row than Norman, Crum, Wolf, Sandowski, and Slater." Jinx was writing the line-up on the big roster card they would use in the dugout.

"Adams better be as good as they say he is," said young Tuffson, who had come to regard third base as his own.

"We aren't letting up on him with the lower end of the line-up, either," Barney said. "Wilkins will hit sixth. Wellington will play right field and hit seventh, and Wade will hit eighth. Once the innings turn over, their job is going to be to get on base ahead of our power. I expect to call on Wilkins, Wellington, and Wade to bunt down the third-base line in any situation, and they're going to run when they get on base. When Adams isn't worrying about lefthanded power, he's going to be worrying about fielding his position and holding the runners."

"I don't know how long you lay awake last night thinking out that line-up, Barney," Jinx said, "but I think it figures to get the first job done—getting us some runs and Adams out of there."

"Adams ain't gonna lie down an' roll over for us," Granny said. "He's the smartest pitcher in baseball. He's got the best assortment of stuff there is. And he'll battle you for everything."

Barney moved down to his end of the aisle and sat down. He nodded. "Let's talk about Adams. Some of you have hit against him in competition—Wade, Crum, and Wellington. Most of us old-timers here know how he works. As Granny says, he's got more good pitches than anybody in baseball, maybe in the history of the game. His big pitch is still his fast ball. It's a moving fast ball, and he can keep it down. He's got a sinking fast ball too—really a quick slider. He'll come with it mainly in double-play situations. His curve is decent, not remarkable, except that he never seems to throw it the same speed twice. He's got an off-speed curve. He's got a sharp screwball, and every once in a while he'll show you his forkball. He uses his screwball and forkball mainly to keep you off stride and guessing. I would say his out pitches are his fast ball and his off-speed curve. He's got enough confidence in his control so he doesn't mind getting behind you. One time he'll waste two pitches on you; and next time he'll blow two quick strikes past you." Barney nodded at Slater. "You've caught him maybe two hundred games, Red. You know how he thinks and works."

Slater rubbed his unshaven jaw with his massive fingers. "I been thinkin' a lot about Jerry, how he works, since we traded him." His voice was squeaky and earnest. "One thing to look for is that he likes to surprise you by throwing the same pitch twice in a row. He will set you up with a fast ball, then come right back with another fast ball, when you're lookin' for a curve. He will slow curve you and come right back with a slow curve. He likes to call his own game. I worked with him so much, I got so I could think with him, but even then he used to shake me off a lot. Today he's going to be working against most of us for the first time, so he'll be going more with his catcher and the book they've got on us. When he shakes off a sign or two, I got an idea he may be wanting to go back to the same pitch he just threw."

"That's what I sayin'," Dandy Crum said. "He throw his hummer to impress you, an' then he come right back with it. He impress you once, you get set to impress *him*. 'Nother thing, now, you men he workin' against the first time, he want you to know all he's got. He want you to see his hummer, his Big Charley. He want you to know he's got the screwball an' the forkball. He want to *impress* you with all his stuff. He got the big reputation, he want you to know he's got the backer-up for it. He want you to be thinkin' so hard what he's throwin' next, you're up there thinkin' 'stead of hittin'.'"

"That's right, Dandy. Bill," Barney said to Wellington, "you hit Adams real good last year."

Wellington gave a shrug and took off his spectacles. "I don't know how I hit when I'm hitting, let alone when I'm not. I don't try to guess any pitcher, least of all Adams. He likes me to chase his outside curve, but he will come right to my power with his fast ball, and he'll throw his screwball in on me tight. I like what Skip says about us righthanders bunting on his low fast stuff. I think we'll do good bunting his low stuff."

"What we're talking about there, as much as getting on base, is his bad right knee," Barney said. "Fielding bunts down the third-base line won't do that knee of his any good."

"It's known around the league," Dandy Crum said. "Pretty soon everybody be bunting him down the third-base line, get him outa there and send him a get-well card."

"We'll give him a chance to put his weight on it, anyway," Barney said.

The players looked into their hands. They saw the pattern of their engagement more clearly and understood the implacability of their leader. Their spirits rose.

"Who's he gonna send get-well cards to?" Granny asked. "He'll hit back."

The players looked up.

"We don't look for a knock-down party," Barney said, "do we, Bax?"

"He don't throw tight," Baxley said, "except on purpose. Neither do I."

Barney turned to Wolf. "How about you, Granny? How you gonna hit Adams?"

"I'm a singles hitter but enough of a pull hitter, he'll pitch me low and outside. What I look to do against him is slap the ball the other way through the shortstop hole."

"Big Don?"

"As lead-off man, am I supposed to get on base or swing long?"

"Long."

"I'll pick me a pitch and give it a riffle."

"Wade?"

The shortstop was a hard man with a round face. "I didn't have too much success against Adams, so maybe I'm not the one to say it, but I think that Jerry's best pitch is his reputation. There's harder throwers in this league. You've seen better curve balls. What you haven't seen is anybody with his reputation, confidence, and control. If we think of him as just another man out there, maybe we'll hit him like just another man out there. One thing, his fast ball isn't near what it was three years ago. He can't overpower you the way he used to."

"The air out there today is going to take a little more off his fast ball," Barney said, "but we can look for his curve to break sharply. It may take an inning or two for him to realize his fast ball doesn't quite have it today. If he blows a fast ball past you, get set for another one. Remember what Red told us: if he shakes off a sign or two, he may be coming back with the same pitch he just threw." He turned to Jinx Moore, the batting coach. "Does that about cover it, Jinx?"

"On Adams."

"Now," Barney said, "I want to give you our defensive deployment for today. As you know, the wind is blowing strong and steady diagonally in from the left-field corner. It will not change much during the game. You can count on the wind. I want the left and center outfielders to play in two or three steps closer on every batter than they normally would. I want the relay men to go three or four steps further into the outfield than normal on all relay plays. Throw low and hard. A long throw will fade off and die on you."

Much earlier in his life, at seven o'clock in the morning, Barney had awakened with the memory of defeat and a sense of despair. Now the memory and sense returned and fought against the rising confidence he felt as the leader of the men he had emboldened. His despair was in himself; his confidence in his men. He breathed deeply. The game would never start, but the day would end.

Dee Wilkins, a young Negro of goodness whose force was purposeful only on the field of play, raised his hand like a boy in school. Dee had sweated away the booze of his night, and his eyes now focused sharply on what they saw. Barney, to whom the game was life, nodded at the young player to whom the game was a way out. "Yes, Dee?"

"Let me get this, Skip. You want I play a hitter like I always play him but *in* on him two-three steps."

"That's right. Make them hit the ball over your head."

"Okay, now then, with the wind to right, I normally play two-three steps with the drift of the wind. You want me play in *and* two-three steps both?"

"Not today, Dee. You play like there was no wind at all, because you've got to be looking to give Dandy some help in left. And you, Bill"—turning to Wellington—"will have that much more ground to cover in right." Their weakened defense smote him. "You've both got the wheels to do it."

Dandy Crum shook his head. "I get over there pretty good, Skip. He don't have to cheat to me too much."

"I'll *be* there," Dee told Dandy.

"Takes but one glove to haul it in," Dandy said. "Give me room."

The player who did not smile was Ted Jones, a member of the Old Line who had been a sure starter in the outfield before Barney had come up with the fleeter and stronger young Negroes. He was a switch-hitter who could bat left against Adams; he could cover almost as much ground as Wilkins and Wellington; he had an arm; he was the only Old Liner on the bench for today's game. Barney looked into his eyes. Each, but no one else, saw the anguish of the other. Somewhere there are nine guys, Barney thought, going out to play ball on a Sunday afternoon for the fun of it, but that ain't us.

"Now, Cronk," he said, turning to Ed Cronkite, his thinking coach, "get the projector ready and we'll take a look at the diagrams on these hitters, and Bax will tell us how he's gonna get them out today."

When he had taken over as manager the season before, Barney had started a system of recording on diagrams what every batter on the nine other teams in the league—nearly two hundred and fifty altogether—did every time he came to bat against every pitcher of the Blue Jays he faced. The system had grown out of ideas he and Ed Cronkite had talked about when they were both players. Cronkite had then been the second catcher, behind Slater. As an intelligent and energetic man who did not get a chance to play every day, he had devoted himself to a conscientious study of the strengths, weaknesses, and probabilities of the opposing hitters. He saw and remembered so much that he became able to predict. Barney understood that prediction was the purpose of acquiring experience. He retired Cronkite as a player and put him in charge of remembering. On a sketch of the playing field, Cronkite traced and recorded every hit or out a player made against each of the Blue Jay pitchers, each of whom was designated by a color. If the batter hit to shortstop against Baxley, a red line was drawn on the diagram to short. If he hit a ground ball past short into left field, a red line was drawn into left field, ending in a symbol indicating a single. If he hit a fly ball to left field against Pasquale, a green dotted line was entered; if the ball was hit in the air into left field safely, a green dotted line with a symbol for a single was entered. Doubles, triples, and home runs were recorded, along with bunt singles and sacrifice bunts and fly balls, foul balls that were caught, strikeouts, walks, and hit-by-the-pitcher. Now they had diagrams on all hitters, going back into last season.

Baxley was a pitcher, not a thinker. To him a batter was a man with an inadequate stick in his hands. His lower face was perpetually burned by sun and wind, from working in the fields as a boy and on the mound as a man; his forehead and bald spot were dead white. The beak of his cap and his hawk nose and sharp chin seemed to opposing batters to be appendages on an otherwise faceless and emotionless scarecrow. Now he took his place behind the projector beside Cronkite and looked at the Warriors' line-up card Jinx had given him.

The room was darkened, and the diagram of Hochstein, the second baseman, a lefthanded batter, was on the screen. It showed that he was a successful batter who usually hit the ball up the middle, as often to the left side of second base as to the right. He was more likely to ground out than fly out. He rarely bunted or struck out. Most of his hits were singles between left center and right center. The red lines, indicating his performance against Baxley, showed that he was most likely to ground out to the shortstop or second baseman. He had got only four hits, line singles, off Baxley.

"I keep him loose. I pitch him tight and make him give ground to the curve. He don't bother me too much," Baxley said.

"He's a first-ball hitter," Cronkite said.

"He won't hit *my* first pitch," Baxley said, "except on his back."

"Play him straight away," Cronkite said.

"Even more shallow than usual in the outfield today," Barney put in.

Now the diagram for Black, a .300 righthanded hitter who had been playing center field for the Warriors for ten years, was on the screen. He was a spray hitter whose hits were fanned out from the left-field line to the right-field line. His long balls were all to left and center. He also bunted a good deal, both to advance a runner and to get on base. He had walked against Baxley more than against any other pitcher and had hit three home runs off him.

"This fella, to me he's the best hitter they got," Baxley said. "I work him careful, fast stuff away and a high curve in to his hands. He golfs low stuff pretty good. Play him to left, though he can go the other way."

"Play him normally deep in left," Barney said, "but in on him in right and center."

"He's very fast down the line," Cronkite pointed out. "Notice how many leg hits he gets. The infield can't wait for the ball on him, they got to charge it, especially in a double-play situation."

The next two hitters in the Warriors' line-up, Shepley and Sorenson, were both strong lefthanded power hitters. Baxley said he would curve them and change them and try to keep everything low and away.

"I try to keep the Big Cheese from pulling anything. If there's runners on base, I'll try to get him on low curves away, but I'll jam him first and may try to get him with a high, tight slider."

"He hit a high, tight slider about five hundred feet off you last time out," Barney reminded him, tracing the long red line over the stands.

"It wasn't quick enough," Baxley said. "He ain't gonna know my slider from my fast ball till it's on him today."

And so down the line-up—Amacito, Perdowski, McStay, Anderson, and Adams—and into the bench strength, especially the righthanded batters, Fisk, Costello, and Shassere, who were most likely to be called upon to pinch hit against Baxley, they examined and discussed the probabilities and capabilities of the enemy. In doing so, they strengthened their belief in their ability to win. The main thing was that they had a plan; it might not work, but it was something to work on.

Once in a night club in New York, after their last World Series victory, Barney had been introduced to Maurice Chevalier following his performance. "I don't know what you've got," Barney had told him. "You're not as funny as Bob Hope, and you can't sing with Nat Cole, but I hardly breathed while you were working. You and Al Jolson, whose style is not my style, make me feel as if *I* were working for *you.* What is it?"

"Somebody has described this magic thing between the artist and his friends in front," the Frenchman had said, "as the mysterious contact of the heart."

Now, in the full light of the clubhouse, Barney felt this mysterious contact with his players. They expected a final word from him. If what he said was true, they would take it with them into the game. "There are only nine of us who are going to start this game," he said, "but there are twenty-nine of us here with numbers on our backs. Everything that everyone of us does and says and sees can be a factor in this game. Every one of us has got the other twenty-eight with him. We all got a job to do. Winning this game may be more important to me than it is to any of you. But nobody here is ever going to forget this game. What we give ourselves to remember of this game will depend on how well and how hard we play it. Let's give ourselves a good memory to take with us, wherever we go from here."

He turned and walked to his office and closed the door behind him, certain of himself and his men and their destiny this day. What am I, he asked himself, a yo-yo that goes up and down on the string of my own feelings?

7

Barney stepped up from the dugout into the sunshine and turned to the owner's box, where Johnston
Dudley would be—and was—waiting to get his RSVP.
Lissie was there too. She was a woman of forty who
looked like a woman of fifty who managed through
care and exercise to look like a woman of forty. Her
mouth was hard, her chest was nearly flat, and her
legs were long and beautiful. Their guests were
show-business celebrities and their attachments. One
was the famous night-club and television comedian;
another was a female musical-comedy star of a few
seasons back; another was the lady writer; the other
older woman, with big blue eyes and silver hair, had
to be the heiress who wanted Wellington to play
with. The others were an assortment of young people who wore sunglasses and amused expressions.
They were named things like Choochoo, Fifi,
Brenda, Denny, Zee, and Freddy. Barney took off his
cap and nodded gravely at each from his side of

the low steel fence. "We're all looking forward to our party tonight, Barney," Lissie said.

Johnston asked, "Are the boys all lined up, Barney?"

"They've got a ball game to think about." He looked around the stands.

Johnston stood up so he and Barney could talk into each other's ears. "Lissie came here with these people and promised them this party. That's what they're here for."

"We're here to play this game," Barney told him. "Nice crowd, maybe go forty thousand."

"This party is important to us and our friends."

Smiling for Johnston and nodding to his friends, he said so they all might hear, "We're looking forward to it, Johnsie. See you all later."

The umpires—Mintz, Britton, Morgan, and Shaughnessy—were waiting at home plate, and Barney walked toward them. As on a signal, Briscoe stepped up from his dugout. They met at the plate. Barney took his line-up from his back pocket and tore off the top card for Shaughnessy, who would be working behind the plate. He gave the second copy to Briscoe and put the third back in his pocket. His starting line-up was now official. Briscoe, as the visiting manager, had the right to study it and make such changes as he chose in his own before submitting it. He looked at Barney's line-up for a moment. His massive humorless face with its deep-set eyes and great drooping jowls, which worked like a metronome on his tobacco, showed no surprise or concern. He handed the original of his set line-up to Shaughnessy and the copy to Barney, who glanced at it and put it in his back pocket with his own.

"Anything about the ground rules anybody wants to take up?" Shaughnessy asked. They had gone over them thoroughly Friday night, the first game of the series.

Briscoe pointed to the long roller against the near left-field fence, on which was rolled the covering for the infield. "Last night Sorenson went up against the roller to make a catch. Has he got the right to jump on top of it to get a ball over his head?"

"No," Barney said. "He can lean against it and reach up and over it as far as he can, but it's like it was part of the fence. He can't climb it."

Shaughnessy took a notebook from his coat pocket and consulted it. "That's an established ground rule for this park." He was a skinny redheaded man with white eyebrows and lashes and blue eyes, who called them quick and walked away tough.

Briscoe looked around the playing field for additional flaws. Then he turned abruptly and walked in his purposeful slouch, head down, to his dugout, where Jerry Adams and his players were waiting.

Barney turned toward the screen behind home plate, where Marianna was sitting with an empty seat beside her and two behind her, as was her wont and her right.

"Ladies and gentlemen," the field announcer's amplified voice called out over every other clamor to every ear in the stadium, "here are the official starting line-ups for today's game. For the Warriors, hitting first and playing second base, Hochstein . . ."

Barney walked to her, and she leaned forward to him until their foreheads were nearly against the wire. Their voices were lost except to each other in the mighty, unheard sound of the ball park. "Get your pencil ready, honey. I got something new and different for Jerry to look at. Partly yours."

"I got a good feeling. I'll go right home, Barney, and get the barbecue ready."

He shook his head. "Dudley is giving a party for some movie-type people. I gotta round up some of the boys and go."

"Oh. The girls—"

"Gotta."

"I wanted you home tonight, Barney. Win or lose."

He resented every intrusion of the world into his game.

"Will it be late?" she asked.

"For God's sakes! I don't know. I'll call you."

"And for the Blue Jays," the announcer proclaimed, "leading off and playing first base, Don Norman . . ."

"Wow," Marianna said, fumbling for her pencil. Her small sound of surprise was echoed and amplified by thousands of other small voices.

"I'll call you after the game," he said.

"Batting second and playing left field, Dandy Crum . . ."

Marianna, all baseball wife now, looked up briefly from her pencil and scorecard and nodded good luck. Barney walked slowly to the dugout and into the game to be played, abstractedly aware of the rising pitch of the crowd's concern and excitement over his anti-Adams line-up. He stepped down into the dugout and called, "Okay, fellows." The starters leaped up the steps at either end and ran to their places (except Baxley, who stalked out deliberately) to an enormous welcome, under which was a bass of boos and over which were a few shrill catcalls of derision from those who resented the departure from a conventional line-up. Barney stood at his place in his corner of the dugout, away from his players, and looked out to the flag in center field, his cap at his heart, in the sudden pealing silence of the organ's "Oh, say, can you see." What he saw was the steady wind of a high-pressure day in June, holding the flag rippling stiff toward the right-field corner, and what he thought was, What will Briscoe and Adams come at me with against what I am going with against them? The fans applauded and cheered, not so much for love of country and its victorious past as for their anticipation of the struggle that was now to commence before their eyes.

8

The contest began as a personal struggle between two of its meanest and most skilled antagonists. Baxley, a cornfield farm hand, pulled his cap down tight over his forehead and raised his head slightly in compensation for the low brim to glare down at Hochstein, an intellectually and muscularly tense Jew from the brick and stone jungles of the Bronx. Barney understood their hatred of one another. Baxley particularly enjoyed his natural advantage as a lefthanded pitcher over Hochstein, a lefthanded batter, and took full advantage of it. His tactics against him were nearly invariable and almost invariably successful: make him back away from high, tight fast balls and get him with a sinking curve ball away or a quick, deceptive slider. Hochstein, a man of temper, did not like to be thrown at by anyone, but it made him wild with rage to be thrown at by an anti-Semitic fundamentalist.

Barney's regret that baseball was a game in which

personal and even racial and religious hatreds were factors on which there were no percentages was mitigated by the competitive assay that his man's hatred was cold and contemptuous while Briscoe's man's hatred was emotional and avenging. Baxley had the advantage of today, Hochstein of some unknown tomorrow.

Scraping the dirt with his spikes until they were firmly but not comfortably set, Hochstein waited for the first pitch. Just before Baxley dipped into his wind-up, the malignant voice of Granny Wolf cut shrilly but privately across the diamond to remind Hochstein that he could expect a ball at his head: "Stick it in the Horn's ear!" Hochstein glowered out toward this new tormentor, and his lips cursed him. Baxley's full wind-up was a graceful swooping forward and down; then back up and down with the pitch, his invisible eyes never leaving their target. The pitch was high and in on Hochstein, who leaned away and toppled a step backward. The ball, a slider, took a quick dip in and caught the inside back corner of the plate. Shaughnessy thrust his arm high in his dramatic strike call. The crowd cheered the strike and the beginning of action. Hochstein picked up a handful of dirt and threw it down angrily while protesting the injustice of the call. "You gonna have another blind day, fish-eater?"

"It slid in there, Horn," Slater said righteously.

The crowd booed its derision of the crybaby. "Stand in there and hit," Shaughnessy told him.

Baxley threw his second pitch at Hochstein's head, a fast ball that hopped in toward the batter. Hochstein was obliged to duck and fall ignominiously away into the dirt. The crowd gasped at the close miss and cheered Baxley's cunning. Baxley, peering down, confirmed Slater's signal for the next pitch, pumped elaborately, and came in with a beautiful slow curve. Hochstein lunged forward, swung deliberately over the ball and with no effort to hit it, and the gleaming bat slipped from his hands and spun like an ancient weapon at his enemy on the mound. Baxley made a leaping dive. The bat whizzed across the mound where his leg had been. Up, Baxley charged Hochstein with cocked fists. Hochstein advanced a stride and squared to meet his enemy. Slater, wise in the situation, sprang past Hochstein and ran with outstretched arms to smother his pitcher's charge and to protect him, not so much from Hochstein's fists as from getting thrown out of the game. Barney, the same thought in mind, bounded up the dugout steps and sprinted to the vortex of action.

Shaughnessy also stepped between Hochstein and the clawing Baxley, as players from the field and both benches converged on the scene, looking for trouble.

Barney grabbed Baxley's other arm. "Get back and simmer down," he told him, patting his rump. Slater, an arm around his pitcher's shoulder, calmly walked him away from the milling players, who were being shooed to their rightful places by the umpires. Shaughnessy got Barney and Briscoe to face him together. "Now that's all, you hear me? We're here to play ball, and we're gonna play ball, if I have to clear both benches and fine the both of ya a month's pay."

"Bax's fast ball must have got away from him," Barney said.

"The bat must have slipped out of Hochstein's hands," Briscoe said.

"We'll play it from here," Shaughnessy said. "You know I mean it."

The crowd thundered its approval of the excitement as the action of the game resumed. Ahead two strikes and a ball, Baxley fired another high fast ball to the inside of the plate. Hochstein swung hard but undercut the ball, and it popped straight up. Slater caught it, standing on the plate. The crowd cheered the easy out and booed Hochstein as he strode to the obscurity of the dugout and thoughts of vengence another time.

Tony Black, next up, was a strong, skinny Negro who batted righthanded and looked at the world and pitched balls for whatever they were, without joy or complaint. Slater signaled for a low fast ball to the outside edge of the plate. But Baxley, feeling his cunning, shook him off and served up a high curve that broke in on Black's swing. Black, leaning slightly away, got the bat to the ball and hit it sharply to center field. Barney judged it in for a single, but Wilkins, dutifully shallow, charged it unhesitatingly at his great speed and made the catch at knee level. Young Messengale in his exuberance leaned forward and shouted down the bench his tribute to Barney's positioning of the defense. "Way to play 'em, Skip!"

Johnny Shepley, a stocky Negro with quick wrists and the speed of a sprinter, the Warriors' most consistent hitter, crouched lefthanded against Baxley. His task, with no runners on base to move along, was to get on base ahead of the power of the Big Cheese, now at rest on one knee in the on-deck circle, like a boulder in a field. Shepley, sure of the strike zone, would test Baxley's control—unless he tried to push a surprise bunt past him or swung hard at the first pitch to his liking. How could you figure Shepley? Baxley's best pitch against him was the sidewheeling low fast ball away from him, which he was most likely to hit on the ground for an infield out. Baxley fired it, but missed outside. Respectfully he tried again and missed again.

Behind on the count, Slater signaled for a curve, and Baxley reluctantly acceded but missed with it, low and outside. Barney involuntarily got to his feet in irritation, stepped forward, turned around, and sat down again. A pecularity of Baxley's was that he had an unlikely but deep respect and admiration for the physical prowess of Negroes; "God made them like He made me an' you," he sometimes said, "only better." Whatever the root and nature of this feeling, Baxley pitched against good Negro hitters fairly, cautiously, and almost fearfully. Now, with a count of three balls and no strikes, he had to throw strikes. They would be fast balls, his strength against Shepley's. Would Briscoe ask Shepley to let the pitch go by, testing Baxley's control, or would he give Shepley permission to swing away at a good pitch in the hopes of an extra-base hit? From the Blue Jays' bench, Briscoe could be seen standing in his dugout, both hands on the rail, staring intently at Quist, his third-base coach, who would give the sign to Shepley. Both hands on the rail—was that the sign? Briscoe took off his cap and wiped his brow with the back of his hand. Was that it? He dropped his right hand from the rail and finally raised his right foot to the top of the dugout.

Jinx Moore called each of these maneuvers to Ed Cronkite, who made notes on his pad. Now Jinx turned his attention to Quist, from whom Shepley was getting his sign. Quist clapped his hands. "Skin," Jinx called. Quist shouted encouragingly to Shepley,

"You can do it, Johnny." "First name," Jinx reported. Quist touched the beak of his cap—"Color"—clapped his hands again—"Skin"—wiped his hand across the letters on his chest—"Color"—and put his hands on his hips briefly before a final clap of the hands. Shepley, instructed, stepped into the batter's box. "Briscoe, one hand down. Quist, color," Jinx said, "like last night—hit away!"

"Switch him to breaking stuff."

Jinx cupped his hands and bellowed out to Baxley, "Blow it past him, Rube." The use of his nickname told Baxley his bench wanted him to throw a curve. Baxley twitched his fingers in his glove in confirmation and decided on a compromise pitch, a slider. As the ball, thrown with care but without real confidence, darted shoulder-high toward the outside of the plate, Shepley swung mightily and connected solidly, driving the ball high and far into the opposite, or left, field.

Barney thought, Why couldn't Baxley hate Negroes instead of Jews? There are more of them in baseball.

On another day Shepley's drive would have been a home run, but the ball, slightly sliced, its spin carrying it toward the foul line, lost its force in the heavy air moving against it, and it died and dropped easily in the sure glove of Dandy Crum, who had been given plenty of time by its long flight to get under it almost against the wall near the Warriors' bullpen. Barney clapped his hands, and the crowd thundered its relief. He waited at the dugout steps for Baxley. "You're working high, Bax," he told him. "The ball didn't touch dirt the whole inning." Baxley's main effectiveness was in getting batters to hit his low pitches on the ground; all three of these outs had been into the air off high pitches.

"I got my stuff," Baxley said shortly. "Get me some runs, Skip."

Barney went out to his place in the third-base coaching box to get some runs against Jerry Adams, his old buddy.

9

Jerry Adams was a handsome black-haired, white-skinned man, Black Irish somewhere in him, who did his best work at night. He did not like the sun and good things of the day. He was a man who liked to sleep late in the cool of the morning and ease into a day toward its evening and darkness, loosening his muscles and gathering strength and spirit for the work and adventures of the night. Night baseball was to his liking; there was no hot sun burning into the thin layer of fat over his smooth, easy muscles; a gulp of night air was refreshing and soothing in his lungs; the black of darkness above the bright arena of the game seemed to be like his own deep calm and confidence surrounding his intense concentration on the batters and the sudden crises of the game; the batters could not pick up the nuances of his assortment of pitches as well as they could in the more pervasively illuminated daytime.

Barney, kicking at the lines and tufts of grass in

the rectangle of his pilothouse, the third-base coaching box, studied Jerry's right knee as it came around in the follow-through of his warm-up pitches. He could not be certain, but he was inclined to believe the slight bulge inside the red and white stocking was a tightly wrapped elastic bandage. Occasionally he raised his eyes to study Jerry's face—calm and intent, as usual. Even though he faced Barney directly for a moment as he set himself in the box for each pitch, Jerry looked through him as if he were an invisible presence. There had been no recognition between them since the day Barney had told him he had been traded for Wellington and Jerry had walked away without shaking hands.

There was an enormous roar of welcome for Big Don Norman as he stepped out of the dugout and advanced toward the plate, swinging two bats to flex and try his muscles. With the welcome in the crowd's thunderous greeting was the recognition of the boldness of the strategy in beginning the attack with the Blue Jays' mightiest hero. Barney felt the crowd's excitement in himself.

Big Don was in the box, standing comfortably still without distinctive mannerisms. Jerry Adams was leaning forward, reading his catcher's signal. Barney was aware, as a moment of baseball, that the two greatest stars of the game, perhaps the only two players now in the National League who would be automatic and unanimous selections for the Hall of Fame when they became eligible, were facing each other as enemies for the first time in their years of baseball. This classic frieze came gracefully to life as Norman swung his bat easily and returned it to cocked position while Adams dipped into his wind-up.

It was an overhand fast ball in on Norman. The big man stepped back, turning away to his right. The ball, thrown with purpose, hit him on his left elbow. It fell, spent, at his feet. Big Don, who was a standard-setter of major-league behavior, looked dumbly at his hurt and then, not recognizing his enemy with curse or glance and ignoring the instinctive temptation to ease the pain of his broken bone with his good hand, trotted majestically to first base.

In the enormousness of the disaster he suspected and feared, Barney sprinted across the diamond to his stricken star. Hank Boller, the chubby white-shirted trainer, was there in an instant. "It hit bone," Big Don said to Barney. In the privacy of the tight protection of Barney, Hank, and Jinx Moore, the Hall-of-Famer put his big right hand carefully under the elbow and raised it slightly for inspection. "I reckon it's busted."

Hank's knowing fingers confirmed the seriousness of the injury. Now they were surrounded completely by the anxious faces of every Blue Jay in uniform.

At the outer edge were the umpires and silent Warriors. Jerry Adams remained impassively on the mound and began to throw easily to his catcher to stay warm and loose during this interruption of play. Hank bound the forearm and elbow with an elastic bandage. "We gotta take him to the hospital for X-ray," he told Barney. "Hold it tight against your chest," he said to Big Don.

Hank on one side, Barney on the other, escorted by the entire squad, Big Don walked slowly toward the dugout, unmindful of the valedictory applause of the standing crowd. Dr. Sanderson, the club physician, who had been watching from his box near the dugout, was waiting for them. "I'll take him in, Hank," he said. "You may be needed here."

Barney put his hand on Big Don's shoulder. The injury was a direct result of the tactics Barney had chosen to destroy Jerry Adams. There was nothing to say. Big Don was out of action for this game and perhaps for many games to come.

"Call me, Doc, as soon as you know."

"It may be just a bad bruise," Dr. Sanderson said, and he and Big Don walked away down the tunnel and over the bridge, while Barney and his players turned again to their game.

"Messengale," Barney said.

The boy was at his side. "It's a hell of a way to break into the line-up, Skip."

Barney looked into his eyes and said, "You can do it, kid."

"Running for Norman and entering the line-up at first base for the Blue Jays," came the field announcer's voice, "Number Eighteen, Messengale."

This announcement evoked an angry and ominous outburst from the crowd—directed at Adams, who was still tossing the ball lazily to his catcher.

"Ladies and gentlemen," the announcer's voice went on, "Don Norman's left elbow is being X-rayed to determine the extent of injury. An announcement will be made as soon as word is received."

The angry voice of the crowd reached a deafening crescendo and slowly subsided as the players resumed their positions and Dandy Crum stepped into the box to face Adams.

Dandy had one of the more elaborate stances in the game; feet rather narrowly spread, he leaned forward from the waist and then sank into a deep crouch. From this position, he was able to take a big stride and a hard level swing at pitches in the lower part of the strike zone and still, using his knees as elevators, come up to swing level at a fast, high curve ball or, his favorite cripple, a high fast ball to the outside of the plate. When he swung and missed, the momentum of his attack spun him around one and a half times.

Adams, unruffled by the anger of the crowd, fired

a fast ball in and on him, the same pitch that had hit
Big Don. Dandy stepped back and turned away to
his left from the ball. It hit him behind his right
shoulder, a glancing blow off the strong neck muscle.
Dandy showed his contempt for Adams by ignoring
the pain and by pausing to toss his bat back toward
the on-deck circle before ambling cheerfully to first
base. The crowd's anger at Adams' deliberate wick-
edness was nearly hysterical. Barney stood poised.
At first base Jinx checked with Dandy and gave Barney a sign that Dandy was not injured. Messengale
trotted down to second base. The players in both
dugouts and on the field were ready to charge, but,
sensing that the game itself was in jeopardy, held
their positions. Shaughnessy, pumping his words out
loudly and distinctly from his chest like an assistant
fire chief calling for more hose, moved to the plate
and summoned Barney and Briscoe to him. "Both of
yez, here now! Mann! Briscoe! Both of yez!" Barney
walked slowly toward him, quickening his pace
when he saw Briscoe trotting up from his dugout.

The meeting was interrupted by another outburst
from the crowd. A buffalo-headed middle-aged man
in a Hawaiian sports shirt was charging from the left-
field foul line toward Jerry Adams. A blue-pantsed
usher brought him down with a flying tackle. The
ushers smothered the fan's spirit and hustled him
off the field to the left-field wagon gate. The crowd

laughed, cheered, applauded, hollered, and booed.

Shaughnessy strode to the field announcer, whose calm voice promptly proclaimed: "Ladies and gentlemen, the Blue Jays are responsible for maintaining conditions under which the game can be played fairly. The umpires have asked us to announce"—a great rise of boos—"that further interruptions on the field of play may result in forfeiture of the game." The crowd yelled angry derision but nevertheless subsided into nervous and excited murmurings.

"Now, then," Shaughnessy told the two managers, "I am going to hold the two of yez and both them pitchers responsible for any more throwing behind the batters." He advanced toward Adams. "I hereby warn you"—pointing dramatically at Adams—"not to throw behind again." Now he advanced toward the Blue Jays' dugout, and his accusing arm rested its sights on Baxley. "And you too, in there, Rube. You are warned." The warnings carried automatic fines of $50 for each of the pitchers. From the Blue Jays' dugout a towel was seen waving, baseball's mute but contemptuous expression of a bad call. Shaughnessy spotted the towel waver. "You. Out!" He advanced to the dugout to make certain the proper culprit left the game. It was Murdock, Barney's young left-handed pitcher; Barney had feared for a sinking moment that it was Kunz, his knuckleball relief specialist.

"Do I make myself clear?" Shaughnessy demanded, returning again to the two managers.

"We ain't done anything," Barney said, "but get hit."

"We don't start anything," Briscoe said. "We finish it."

"*I* will finish it," Shaughnessy said grimly and began to dust off the plate with his whiskbroom.

The two managers looked into each other's eyes.

Barney had spent seven hours coming up with a line-up to shake up Adams coming out, and to destroy him. Briscoe and Adams had looked at the line-up card and, recognizing the soundness of Barney's strategy, had decided to play their own game, not Barney's: we will throw to hit both Norman and Crum (hit, not maim—both pitches were behind the batters, but not at their heads), and we will risk putting two men on base, and we will go on to get the side out; then, our contempt for you and our confidence in ourselves established, we will go on and get everybody out, and pick up the runs we need off your Rube Baxley and a defense that leaks like a sieve.

Okay, Barney thought, and you picked up a bonus by getting Big Don out of my line-up, so now what I'm going to do is get these two runs home and go on from there, according to my plan.

Granny Wolf, the next batter, moved from the on-deck circle, swinging his bat, to the edge of the batter's box. Barney motioned, and they came together, the two whose dislike for each other had never stood in the way of championship play. "I'll move 'em along," Granny said, knowing the situation demanded the bunt.

"Yeah," Barney said, "down the third-base line, make him start putting weight on his bad knee."

"I wanna go the other way," Granny said with his cold and evil grin, "and walk up his back."

Barney considered. Granny intended to bunt down the first-base line and, if it dropped right, crash into and spike Adams when he came over to field the ball. Why not? Granny was the man that could do it, and Granny wanted to do it. "Okay," Barney said. "I'll give you the bunt sign so Crum and Messengale will know that it's on." Granny walked jauntily, swinging his bat, to the batter's box. Barney called him back. "Whattaya think? Let's take the first pitch. They'll probably have a pitchout working, trying to catch Dandy moving away."

Shaughnessy stepped forward again. "Get a hitter up here."

Barney, back in his pilothouse, clapped his hands, wiped his chest, touched his blue cap (the indicator), and clapped his hands—the take sign. Granny slid his right hand to his blue cap, Dandy touched the Blue Jay on his chest, and Messengale straight-

ened a blue stocking in confirmation. Adams, ready
to pitch, stepped off the mound to make Granny
wait, picked up the resin bag, looked in, got his
sign, and fired a fast ball high and outside. Granny
took a stride forward as if intent on driving the ball
out of the park but held his swing in time. The
catcher darted forward to throw, but the runners
were not going any place. Ball one.

Barney gave him the bunt sign: a series of meaningless motions and touches until he wiped across
the Blue Jay on his chest (the indicator) and pulled
his nose. Granny and both runners responded. The
Warriors' infield, obliged to play for the bunt, edged
in. Adams threw a shoulder-high fast ball, a pitch
that a bunting batter is more likely to pop in the
air than tap to the ground. Granny got the bat down
on the ball and drifted it down the first-base line,
a good bunt, but not close enough to the line to give
Granny a chance to crash into Adams, who was over
quick to field it. He picked the ball up barehanded,
took a look, and threw to second in time to get
Dandy out. But Messengale was on third, and
Granny was on first.

There was not a man on his club that Barney
would rather have seen go to the plate against a
righthanded pitcher with a man on third and less
than two out than Sandowski. The fans, too, appre-
ciated the Old Line hero's ability to come through

with a hit or, at least, a fly ball that would permit Messengale of the flying feet to dash home after the catch. The danger—and Adams' purpose—was that Sandowski of the ponderous legs would hit the ball on the ground into a double play. Adams would pitch him low and away. But his first pitch, a low, sharp curve, broke over the plate instead of over its outside corner, and Sandowski hit it hard on the ground down the first-base line. Amacito lunged back at it, but the ball caromed off the bag and skittered, a fair ball in foul territory, toward the Warriors' bullpen for the first hit of the game. Messengale trotted home, and Granny, running with the hit, slid safely into third under Shepley's strong throw. The fans expressed their huge delight by clapping in unison to encourage further scoring.

Now Slater, another Old Line hero who also took more than four seconds to get to first base, had a chance to score the run with a fly ball or a hit that would keep the rally going. But Barney, moving down the box, gave him the bunt sign. Slater had trouble believing the sign. He raised his hand for time and trotted down the line for a conference with Barney. "You got it, Red," Barney told him. "He'll be pitching you low and away to keep you from pulling the ball or hitting it into the air. Drop one down the third-base line."

Slater nodded in sudden appreciation of the move

that figured best to get the run home and put some pressure on Adams' leg. The first pitch was a low screwball, breaking over the outside corner. Slater squared away and tapped it down the line and went lumbering off toward first. Wolf, starting with the pitch, was across the plate before Adams picked up the ball near the line. Adams stopped his lunge and threw to first ahead of Slater.

With two out and Sandowski on second, it was up to Wilkins, the first of the Blue Jays' righthanded batters, to keep it going with a base hit. Wilkins went after the first pitch, a low crossfire fast ball, and fouled it off. He took two pitches for balls before he got his bat on the ball squarely for a hot grounder that McStay came up with and threw to first for the third out.

But two runs were in on only one hit, and the fans wondered aloud as they applauded how the rest of the game could sustain the excitement and drama of the first inning. Barney watched Adams stride to his dugout, wondering what his right knee was telling him.

	1	2	3	4	5	6	7	8	9	R	H	E
WARRIORS	0									0	0	0
BLUE JAYS	2									2	1	0

Cheese Sorenson was Baxley's first problem in the second inning. The Swede, as he was also called, was a second-generation Norwegian from Wisconsin who had been a Big Ten football and basketball star before he had chosen baseball as a life work secondary to dairy farming. He could hit the ball a country mile and throw a clothesline across the diamond. He read books and believed in and spoke up for Jesus, fair play, and the rights of man (especially baseball players).

Barney met Baxley coming out of the dugout. "Tell me you want to throw at Cheese."

"You want I should get the Swede like they got Norman?"

Barney grinned and nodded emphatically. He made a gesture with his right hand past his ear. But his words repudiated the motion. "No, Bax, don't throw at him. I don't want him on base or you out of the game."

"Make up your mind. You want me to throw at him, I'll drop him."

"Pitch him by your book on him."

"Jam him and get him on a low outside curve."

"He's set up for the curve right now. He's watching us. He thinks you've got the word to throw behind him."

Baxley glanced over at the Warriors' dugout and

nodded evil appreciation of his manager's gambit. "He'll come out with a little cowardice in his ass."

Expecting, with reason, that he was fair reprisal for Norman, Cheese took half a step back before he identified the first pitch as a curve breaking away from him. He leaned back in and, with his quick wrists, hit a weak line drive right into Granny Wolf's glove. In his corner, Barney smiled uneasily for the quick out on a pitch that Cheese could easily have driven out of the park. The curve had been carelessly high. Maybe this wasn't one of Baxley's good days.

The batter was Amy Amacito, also a lefthanded power hitter. Baxley, feeling his cunning, shook Slater off until he got his slider. It darted in shoulder-high, and Amacito lifted a high but harmless fly to center. Two pitches, two outs. But Barney's concern deepened. Again the ball had been carelessly high— or Baxley's control was off and he was not able to get the ball down where it belonged.

Against Tootsie Perdowski, Baxley also shook Slater off until he got what he wanted—a screwball breaking away from the righthanded batter. It also hung high, and Tootsie drove it deep to center. Wilkins brought it in after a hard chase.

Barney was on the steps to meet Baxley. "Your breaking stuff is hanging high."

"I got the side out on three pitches, Skip. What else you want?"

"Every pitch could have been hit out of here. All six outs have been in the air. You're a low-ball pitcher, Bax. Let's get 'em out on the ground."

"I got my stuff," Baxley said shortly and went past him to get a sip of water.

"Three pitches, three outs," young Messengale called as he trotted up. "The ball didn't touch the ground, and the catcher didn't handle the ball. Is that a record?"

"I don't think it's a record, but I never saw it before," Barney said.

"Musta happened many times, but I don't remember seeing it before," Jinx said.

"I had an inning like that once in Winnipeg," said Silent Joe Kerwin. "No, I didn't neither; the last out was a pop-up the catcher handled."

Barney turned away from this aimless chatter and went out to watch Jerry Adams take his warm-up tosses. He could see no sign of pain or strain, but Jerry had a long way to go.

Under and over the stir that ruffled the crowd when Adams and Wellington stood poised against each other for the first time since the trade were boos of derision from those fans who took the occasion to express their opinion that the trade stank. A few players in both dugouts shifted their places or stepped forward, the better to see every fine point of this personal battle in the developing struggle.

Wellington was a batter, going good, who got himself set, feet rather widely planted, and waited easily for the pitcher to throw. Now he betrayed the intensity of his desire by scraping his spikes to find a more secure place in the dirt and by swinging his bat to loosen his muscles. Adams, rubbing the ball, turned his back and looked out over his defense before, with easy nonchalance, he looked down and in.

Barney had given Wellington the bunt sign. Now he gave it again. This was the newest sign devised by Jinx to deceive the Warriors if they were reading Barney's signs: bunt-on-bunt took bunt off. Barney hoped Wellington would bunt, but the kid was on his own up there. Hochstein at second and McStay at short were playing normally deep, but Sorenson at third and Amacito at first, responding to a sign from Briscoe, edged in to guard against a bunt.

The first pitch was a low inside fast ball. Wellington made no move except to glare briefly at Shaughnessy when he called it a strike. Adams threw again to the same spot. Wellington watched it go by, just inside. Bear Anderson, the Warriors' catcher, said something to Shaughnessy when he called it a ball. Wellington looked to Barney, who gave him the bunt sign—twice: still on your own up there, kid. "Hang in there! You can do it, Bill," Barney called. Again Adams pitched a low crossfire fast ball. Again Wellington watched it. Two strikes, and Wellington could not now risk a bunt attempt, since a foul bunt with two strikes is a third strike and out.

Sorenson and Amacito moved comfortably back to normal depth. Barney clapped his hands encouragingly to conceal his disappointment. Adams had challenged Wellington three times, and the kid had not taken the bat off his shoulder. Now Adams had him set up to take him at his pleasure. His pleasure was a high, wildly motionless forkball that came in looping downward with its seam showing. Wellington, suddenly in motion, chopped the ball downward, a swinging bunt, and was three strides toward first base before the surprised defensive players could make a move. The ball, driven hard into the dirt in front of the plate, took a high bounce. Many in the crowd mistook it for a little pop fly. Bear Anderson may have thought so too. He charged and dove to get his mitt under it, as Adams and Sorenson, who had seen the play perfectly, ran forward to field the short second bounce. Anderson's belly slide carried him into Adams, who stumbled across him as he reached barehanded for the ball, which bounced past him. Sorenson halted his rush in time to field the ball and prevent Wellington from trying for second. The crowd howled its delight for Wellington's successful daring and speed. Adams, up fast (but with a grass stain on his right knee), called an angry word at his dumb catcher and stalked firmly back to the mound. Barney, as exuberant as a fan at the play's success, began to think out his next move.

Wade was coming to the plate. He swung a bat as a woodsman swings an ax—to strike precisely and knowingly. It was a difficult situation for Adams and the Warriors. Wellington must be held close to first base lest he steal second. They must guard against the bunt-and-run, which meant that both Sorenson and Amacito must play in close, charging or ready to charge. This defense, however, opened holes in their infield between both third and short and second and first and (a) made them vulnerable to the hit-and-run and (b) reduced their best chance for their best hope: a double play. Briscoe's situation was difficult but simple: he must defend against the bunt-and-run.

Barney's situation was advantageous but complex. His fastest runner was at first, and his most dependable and versatile batter was at the plate. Dismissing less favorable alernatives, he reduced his decision to one of two choices: bunt-and-run, which was most likely to advance Wellington to scoring position at second but which was quite likely to cost them an out; and hit-and-run, which offered the best possibility of advancing Wellington all the way to third and getting Wade safely on at first, but which was less likely to be completed successfully. The hit-and-run was made more attractive by the fact that Baxley, who was not likely to get a hit that would enable Wellington to score from second, was the next batter. With a two-run lead, Barney was in a position to gamble, but with his concern for Baxley's failure to keep the ball down and his awareness of the weak defense behind Baxley, he decided to play for one run as if it were the big run of the game: bunt-and-run. In the end, he came up with the very offensive tactic that Briscoe was defending against.

But first he must guard against a pitchout. He gave Wade the take sign. Adams got his sign and threw high and wide where his catcher, pouncing out, could fire to first or second to catch Wellington if he broke from first. Wade took the pitch as if he were ready to swing. Wellington trotted back. Ball one. I got an idea you got so much confidence in your control, you'll try me with another pitchout, Barney thought at Adams. He gave the sign for another take. Again the pitch was high and outside, and again Anderson was in front of the plate with the ball and no place to throw it, except back to Adams.

Ball two, and time to throw strikes, Jerry. What kind of strikes are you going to throw, Jerry? Low strikes that can be bunted, if Wade is up there to bunt? High strikes that can be hit safely, if Wade is up there to hit? What kind of strikes are you going to throw, Jerry?

Adams removed his cap and mopped his forehead with his sleeve and turned around and picked up the resin bag to dry his pitching fingers and to think. He thought through to the weakness in Barney's situation: Baxley as the next hitter. A sacrifice bunt would put Wellington in scoring position at second with one out and with Baxley up to be the big fat second out. Adams would decide to pitch low and give Wade the bunt; besides, if Wade should be swinging on the hit-and-run, a low pitch was more likely to give the Warriors a double play and to end the scoring threat.

In the convolution of a thought, Barney saw his bright prospect of a moment before change to one of failure, but he rejected the temptation to switch to hit-and-run. Adams, his confidence based on the certainty he would make the pitch he decided to make, was again in control of the situation. *But, Jerry baby, you are going to have to make the play on the bunt. How many more plays like that does your seventh-inning knee have in it?*

Adams was ready. Wade was ready. Adams threw quickly to first. Wellington dove his body's length back to the bag, got up, and took another long, dancing lead. Adams was ready. Wade was ready. Adams fired his low, hopping fast ball. Wade, around to face the pitch, let his bat push the ball up the third-base line and, in the same motion, was off toward first. Adams charged the ball and took a look when he got it. Wellington was streaking to second and Wade to first. Adams calmly threw to first to get Wade.

The crowd cheered Wade for his perfect sacrifice and chanted go-go and clapped its eighty thousand hands in a unified appeal to get the run home.

Some of the heart went out of the crowd's exuberant appeal when it saw that the next batter was only Baxley. It applauded him as the hero of their defense and implored him to surprise them with a hit.

Baxley believed in his ability to hit, and he went to the plate with a vision of himself as a pitcher who could win his own ball game. Adams saw him as an aggressive and experienced lefthanded batter with a bat on his shoulder who must be set down as the second out of the inning. He pitched carefully. He missed outside with a fast ball. He thought he got the second one in there. So did Barney. So did Anderson, the catcher. But Shaughnessy called it ball two. Now Adams missed low with a fast ball in to Baxley, and he was in the ticklish position of having three balls and no strikes on a weak hitter.

Barney gave Baxley the sign to take the next pitch, which Adams fired down the middle. And the next. Now Baxley, on his own again, swung hard and fouled off four pitches in a row before lifting a little fly that Hochstein took back of second. *That was a lot of work in the hot sun, Jerry baby, to get a weak-hitting pitcher.*

Messengale, at the plate for the first time, also waited and fouled until the count was three balls and two strikes. He hit a low inside pitch (which might have been ball four and given Dandy Crum a chance to drive the runs home) sharply on the ground. It darted between Hochstein and Amacito. Wellington, flying with the pitch, picked up Barney windmilling him home, and raced to try to score ahead of Shepley's hard straight throw from right field. The ball was in Anderson's mitt as Wellington slid hard. Shaughnessy's arm was cocked for the out sign when the ball trickled idly out of Anderson's grasp. The run was home on the error. The crowd cheered Wellington as he trotted to the dugout. Adams angrily turned his back on his faulty catcher and picked up the resin bag. He still had Crum to get out.

Adams cut loose with the fastest pitch he had thrown. Dandy took it for strike one, but he touched off the next fast ball and hit it into deep center—but

it died as it flew, and Tony Black with a good jump
sped back and took it in.

	1	2	3	4	5	6	7	8	9	R	H	E
WARRIORS	0	0								0	0	1
BLUE JAYS	2	1								3	3	0

Baxley had the bottom of the line-up—McStay,
Anderson, and Adams—to get out in the third. His
ball was moving, but his control was not sharp,
especially with his low pitches. He got behind on
McStay, missing with his low curve, and walked
him for a bad beginning. Then he diddled around
with Bear Anderson, who finally belted a hanging
3-2 curve deep into left center, where only two or
three fielders in baseball other than Wilkins could
have shagged it down. McStay, advancing to second,
just did beat Wilkins' strong throw back to first.
Briscoe was staying with Adams, who came up to
hit for himself. Baxley went after his second out and
got two quick strikes on Adams, who had the bad
luck to drive the third pitch, a careless 0-2 fast ball
down the middle, on a line into the left-field corner.
It was foul by a foot. Adams had to run it out and
come all the way back, winded, to complete his
turn at bat. He hit a sharp grounder to Wade, who
tossed to Wolf, who made a teasingly slow throw to

Messengale to keep Adams running. The double play got Baxley easily out of the inning. Besides, he had, without intent, obliged Adams to run hard twice making the last out.

Anderson took a long time getting his gear back on to give Adams more time to breathe easy and cool down before facing Wolf, Sandowski, and Slater.

"Pour it on," Barney told his incoming heroes as he went out to direct traffic.

Granny Wolf had no friends in baseball. A friend today is an enemy tomorrow, but just a player on your team today is just a player on an opposing team tomorrow. Keep it that way. As lead-off man, he had no obligation except to get on base and sweeten his batting average. He chose, however, to continue and to try to complete the destruction of Jerry Adams. To him this had become the game. There was no sentiment in his effort—no dislike for Jerry Adams, desire for revenge for the maiming of Don Norman, loyalty to his club, or pride in his ability. He was simply interested in seeing it done. Baseball was his life. He intended and expected to be a major-league manager. He never before had taken part in so deliberate and intelligent an effort to win a game by the psychological and physical harassment and destruction of an opponent. As he had looked at today's game in the morning, he had not seen how Barney, caught in the downward spiral of a slump and committed to his kids, could do anything against Adams, Briscoe, and the resourceful Warriors but take another brave beating. His own role was to play it straight and to be on hand to pick up the pieces and put them together into a winning combination when called upon. He had seen clearly and instantly the brilliance of Barney's strategy. It might work; it could; it had to be tried. Granny Wolf could learn something from it.

So Granny bunted down the third-base line. Adams stumbled as he picked it up and fell to his knees. But he was able to right himself and throw hard to Amacito to nip Granny by half a stride. Adams stood for a moment, dusting the dirt from his uniform. *Are you dusting, Jerry baby, or are you giving your seventh-inning knee a sneak massage?*

There was a tight furrow between Jerry's eyes as he looked in on his catcher's suggestion for a pitch to Sandowski. His fingers in his glove, twitching off the signs, expressed anger that was rising to rage. *We're getting to you, Jerry baby.* Sandowski was a reliable hitter because he always expected and was always set to trigger off a fast ball: you can be set for the fast ball and adjust to the unexpected curve or change-up, but you cannot look for a slow pitch and get around on a fast ball. This was Sandowski's philosophy, and his life was full of happy surprises.

Adams came in with the pitch Sandowski would

not expect: the slow, sharply dropping curve into the inside corner. Sandowski, happily surprised, golfed it far into right field, a looping liner just over Shepley's leaping try against the screen. The ball hit solid and darted back into the field, with Shepley racing back in for it. Big Sandowski, a hero at the plate, knew a two-base hit when he had one, and he rounded first and chugged toward second like a clown against one of the best arms in the business. But Shepley juggled the ball an instant before he had it gripped for throwing, and the big man was in safe at second under the tag with a graceful falling hook slide.

The extra base put extra heat under Jerry's anger. He had Slater to pitch to. Swinging confidently and furiously at everything Jerry threw, Slater fouled off two low fast balls, took a curve and a change that missed outside, and golfed the brother of Sandowski's drive to the right-field screen. Sandowski, holding to see whether the ball would be caught, slowly got going under his best head of steam. Barney gambled and waved him on home. Shepley made a quick recovery and a perfect throw that caught Sandowski at the plate. The crowd's wild yell of excitement ended in a groan and a few boos for Barney's witless recklessness in sending a slow man home against Shepley's arm.

So Adams was reprieved: two back-to-back doubles left him unscored upon with a chance to get the third out against a righthanded batter, Wilkins. The furrow jumped from Jerry's forehead to Barney's.

Wilkins went up there to hit, and he sliced an outside low curve for a fly ball that dropped in right center between Shepley and Black. There was no play for Slater at the plate, and Wilkins was standing on second.

Now Wellington was at the plate to complete the destruction of Jerry Adams. *Wellington's gonna knock you out of there, Jerry baby.*

But Briscoe came rumbling out to see how it was with his pitcher. From the dugout steps he motioned to his bullpen, and two righthanders—Jack Massucci, the Warriors' regular long man, and young Terry Wilson, an occasional starter—got up and began to throw. Why two righthanders? Against a strong left-handed hitting line-up, why was Briscoe warming up *two* righthanders? Barney could not see to the bottom of Briscoe's mind on that move.

Sorenson, the team captain, and Anderson, the catcher, came to the mound and were waiting with Jerry when Briscoe came up, kicking at the dirt.

He's hurt, Barney thought with Briscoe. Let's get him out of here. Why risk a great pitcher on a lost game? Barney watched their faces, not so much reading their lips as thinking their minds.

Briscoe said something short and dumb, the only thing possible: "You okay?"

"I ain't happy, but I'm okay," Jerry said in his offhand wry way, what he would.

"I gotta save you for another day," Briscoe said.

"I'm fine. I don't run from him or anybody else." Meaning me, Barney thought.

"This game means more to him than it does to us."

"Not to me it doesn't."

"How's your knee?"

"It's fine."

Briscoe looked out to center field and the scoreboard. You can't take him out, Barney thought, like he was just anybody with a number on his back. "You got a game to pitch out of," Briscoe said. "I got a pennant to win. I can't take a chance."

Jerry shook him off. "Don't ask me to give you the ball."

Sometimes the right thing to do is to go with a man when he is wrong. "Go get 'em, Jerry," Briscoe said and patted his rump and left him there alone with the ball.

Barney Mann clapped his hands and shouted down the line, "You can do it, Bill. Pour it on!" Make my trade look good. The kid looked looser and more confident at the plate than he had since his slump had worsened into the paralyzing effort to break out of it. Jerry, too, seemed to have cooled down to his usual deliberate and forceful cunning. The duel began.

Wellington missed a high curve for one strike and took a low fast ball for another. He had to fall back from an inside fast ball. He followed a low curve all the way in and laid off for ball two. He hit the next fast ball squarely but on a line to Sorenson for the third out.

The rally and the inning were over. Three doubles had produced only one run. Adams was still alive. Were the luck and the surge of the game swinging to Adams and Briscoe?

	1	2	3	4	5	6	7	8	9	R	H	E
WARRIORS	0	0	0							0	0	1
BLUE JAYS	2	1	1							4	6	0

Baxley pitched his best inning. He struck out Hochstein and got Black and Shepley to hit on the ground.

The field announcer's voice calmly told the crowd that the X-ray showed that a bone had been chipped in Don Norman's left elbow and that he was expected to be out of the line-up for two weeks.

The crowd greeted Adams, coming out to pitch the fourth, with a boo-kay of hatred.

Wade jolted Adams by stroking his first pitch up the middle for a single. *You're through, Jerry baby.*

We've got you now. And we'll give you another bunt to field.

Baxley fouled off his first two attempts, but Barney persisted even with two strikes, and the Rube dropped a beauty down the first-base line. Jerry was slow getting to it, and he had no chance to get Wade going to second, so he had to throw to first.

Messengale wanted to be the one to kill the tiring old man. He felt he had him, and he would not be fooled by his cunning. He laid off the first pitch, a low outside fast ball, and was rewarded when Shaughnessy called it a ball. He expected the next pitch in the same spot, and that's where it came for ball two. Anderson protested the call as vigorously as he dared and walked halfway to the mound to toss the ball to his pitcher and to steady him.

Messengale was now the big out for Adams. If he could get him, he had a good chance for an easy inning. With an easy inning behind him, he could hang on and hope the Warriors would get him some runs. He could survive.

This pitch or the next pitch could decide the game. If the kid knew what to do, he could get Adams out of there. If not, he was an easy ground out to second or short. Barney signaled for a conference and met the kid halfway.

"He'll throw a strike," Barney said, kicking the dirt.

"Yeah." The boy nodded.

"Most likely a fast ball low and away."

"Yeah."

"Otherwise a breaking pitch high and tight."

"Yeah."

"What do you figure to do?"

"Go with the pitch."

"You're on your own."

"You want me to bunt on him?"

"If he pitches you low, it's your best shot."

"High?"

"Touch it off."

"Okay, Skip."

"You can do it."

Adams fired a low, fast ball, and Messengale tapped a darting bunt between Adams and the third-base line. Adams leaped to make the play. Stretching to reach the ball, his right leg caved in, and he fell forward.

On his belly with the useless ball, he saw the way to make the play that there was no way to make. He tossed to Sorenson, and Sorenson, his bright Norwegian eyes glittering in instant recognition, stepped in to pick it out of the air barehanded and fire it on a straight line across the diamond to Amacito, who took it for the out by half a step without knowing how it got to him. Wade came on to third.

Jerry's fall had plunged him almost at Barney's

feet, but it was not Barney's place to offer a hand. Jerry got up quickly. For a moment, once, they looked into each other's eyes. Jerry walked back to the mound. He had got his big out. If he got Old Dandy Crum, he could walk to his dugout still in the game. He looked down and in for his sign.

But young Dave Messengale's bunt had finished Jerry Adams. He tried a forkball on Dandy, but it was in the dirt. He missed outside with an imitation of his fast ball. He came in with a curve ball for a strike and followed it with a slower curve. Dandy hit it on top of the right-field stands.

"He Big Charley me once," Dandy said as Barney took his hand going by, "I Big Charley *him.*"

Every fan in the stands and every Blue Jay on the bench was on his feet to applaud the old man as he trotted loosely to the dugout.

Jerry Adams was through. Briscoe came out, signaling for his young righthander. Jerry stood silent in the group at the mound until the boy Wilson got there. Then he gave him the ball and headed for the dugout. Many fans cheered his defeat and booed their hatred of the traitor who had struck down Don Norman. Only a few, remembering his hundred victories on this field and in recognition that he had played courageously and well today, applauded his effort. Barney could not. He picked out his wife in her box behind the plate. She did.

10

With Wolf, Sandowski, and Slater coming up, why had Briscoe come in with the young righthander? With a six-run lead and Adams out of the game, Barney had been about to make his defensive substitutions. But if Briscoe was coming in with righthanders, Barney was going to stay with lefthanded power.

Wolf got his first hit on the youngster's first pitch, a fly ball single to right that Perdowski could not quite reach (but could have, Barney thought, if he had been playing the thick air). Sandowski hit a 2-2 fast ball into center that rolled to the wall and would have been a triple for a faster runner. There was no effort to keep Wolf from scoring. Wilkins grounded out to Hochstein to end the inning, but the Blue Jays went out to the field leading 7 to 0, with Adams out of the game, and with Baxley still working on his no-hitter.

	1	2	3	4	5	6	7	8	9	R	H	E
WARRIORS	0	0	0	0						0	0	1
BLUE JAYS	2	1	1	3						7	10	0

Looking back, Barney saw that his effort to win had been successful. Looking ahead, he saw an unfinished ball game. You can look forward, but you can see only behind you.

Instead of sitting in his corner, alone and contained by the knowledge that each pitch could change the nature and course of the game, he now paced from one end of the dugout to the other, stopping to watch each pitch Baxley made. A walk would not hurt them; a home run would not be a disaster. But he paced and watched.

The Rube had his stuff, no doubt about it. His ball moved, and no two pitches were quite alike. But he was not pitching his usual game. Why wasn't he keeping the ball *down*? With a seven-run lead, why did he seem to be battling each hitter for a strike-out? Why couldn't he deliver a normal, competent, in-command performance, which was all—and precisely—what was needed?

Barney's peevish pacing put an end to the relaxed banter and small jokes that had begun to crop up on the bench. The players concentrated as if the game hung on every pitch. This was no laugher.

Baxley pitched Sorenson like a violinist playing a fiddle. He jammed him, low curve, low outside fast ball—one ball and two strikes—now the drifting outside curve, which Sorenson had to chase to protect the plate. He poked it up the middle. Wade, making a good play of it, got his glove on the ball, dropped it, picked it up, and just missed catching Sorenson at first.

"There goes the Rube's no-hitter," said someone.

Barney hoped so. Maybe it was his dream of a no-hitter that kept Baxley from settling down to his usual competency. But the scorekeeper called it an error on Wade. "Not a good call," the bench agreed, but Baxley's witless no-hitter was still working.

Amacito, another lefty, was no particular threat if Baxley gave him nothing to pull. Baxley gave him nothing. He fooled around and walked him. Now the double-play ball, Bax. And Perdowski hit the ball on an easy bounce to Sandowski, who stepped on third and threw the ball into right center field instead of to Wolf at second. So there were Amacito on third and Perdowski on second with one out. McStay hit a short fly to left, which Dandy charged and caught nicely.

Quist, coaching at third, challenged the old man's arm and sent Amacito in. Dandy got the ball away quickly and accurately, but without much force, and

Amacito slid in under the throw for the Warriors' first run.

After Anderson hit a routine fly to center, Baxley came strutting in with his no-hitter still working.

The run bothered Barney more than a run scored with base hits. It was symptomatic of his weakness up his left side and middle. He could plug the holes in a hurry by moving Wellington to left and putting Jeff or Ted Jones in right, Tuffson at third, and Brooks at second. If Briscoe had come in with a left-handed pitcher, Barney would have made the changes immediately. He was nagged by the fact that his unbalanced original line-up left him with an unbalanced bench. Aside from Ted Jones, a switch-hitter, the only lefthanded batter (except for pitchers) that Barney had on his bench was young Len Michaels, the third catcher who had got only two singles in twenty times at bat. He was nagged too because he was not able to track with Briscoe's thinking in coming in with righthanded pitching against his lefthanded power.

"You'd never guess, lookin' at him," Baxley said to Slater, "that we give him a seven-to-one lead an' I got a no-hitter workin'."

"You lose nine in a row, you lose more than ball games," Slater said.

"At the clubhouse meeting, he looked like he already had this game won. Now he looks like you could chase him out of the park by spitting tobacco juice at his feet."

Dave Messengale went to the water cooler to get away from this talk about their skipper.

Wellington, waiting for a ball he could pull, got behind 1-2 and took a good cut at a high fast ball but popped it almost straight up.

Wade made the kid work to a 3-2 count and then hit a short fly ball that dropped in front of Black for a single. Again Barney called on Baxley to sacrifice, but he fouled three bunt attempts and went back to the dugout to conserve his strength for the protection of his no-hitter. Messengale, the first of the power lefties in Barney's line-up, hit a soaring but dying fly 410 feet to center, where Black gathered it in.

	1	2	3	4	5	6	7	8	9	R	H	E
WARRIORS	0	0	0	0	1					1	0	1
BLUE JAYS	2	1	1	3	0					7	11	2

Barney was tempted to make his defense changes right now—Ted Jones for Crum, Brooks for Wolf, Tuffson for Sandowski—but Crum, Wolf, and Sandowski would bat in the sixth. His lefthanders had hit the kid Wilson good in the fourth, and Messengale had just hit a home run (on a day of lighter air) off him. "Briscoe is asking for a diet of lefthanded power," Barney said to Cronkite and Moore. "We'll give it to him."

"The way Bax is going," Cronkite said, "we've got time."

Briscoe made his next move by sending Shassere, never a star but an established major-league out-fielder, up to hit for his kid pitcher. Throwing in the bullpen, though, was Massucci, another right-hander, so Barney held to his decision to take a chance with his present defense and give his old lefthanders another inning at bat.

Shassere, a righthanded batter, ended Baxley's no-hitter with a sharp single over second.

Against Hochstein, whom he had learned to intim-idate and infuriate, Baxley fired his customary brush-back pitch. It was tight but not on him, and Hochstein ripped into it with sudden and vengeful savagery—a low line drive headed for right field. Messengale leaped for the ball and knocked it down. Then, falling but still trying for an out, he snapped an underhand throw, trying to force Shassere slid-ing into second. His throw skipped into the dirt past Wolf, and the ball bounded into left field. When Dandy Crum got to the ball, Shassere was going into third and Hochstein into second, on a hit and an error on Messengale's throw.

Messengale had made a good play that went wrong. Dandy was a reckoned risk. But who was this fella Baxley pitching today? You can know a man a long time and be with him every day, and a day will come when he will be a stranger to you all day long. Barney went out to talk to the Rube. Some of the fans automatically booed his appearance. Slater trotted up to join the conference, and the infield drifted in.

"I'm strong," Baxley said. "I got my stuff."

"What did Shassere hit?"

"A good pitch. A slider. Hochstein, it was a brush-back, not on him enough."

"Your book on Shassere is keep it low."

"Yeah, it got away from me. Them runners should only be on first and second."

Now that he had blown his chance for no-hit fame and was again just a hard-working pitcher trying to hang on to slim pickings, Baxley could be indomitable. He had good stuff and good courage, and he responded to challenges. He was not wise enough to perform well when he was comfortably ahead nor imaginative enough to make fancy mistakes or go into a panic when he had to pitch to survive. Suddenly Barney warmed to Baxley, as if he were a person. "It's still yours to win or lose, Bax." In baseball, the opportunity to win or lose is all a player can ask for—and all that he can be given.

The Rube said, "I got my stuff."

"Throw strikes with something on them."

First base was open, and Tony Black was up with a chance to drive in two runs. On deck was Shepley.

"I could put Black on and get Shepley to hit it on the ground," Baxley suggested.

"With our lead, we're not giving 'em any base-runners. Pitch to Black." As suddenly as he had warmed up to Baxley, Barney cooled on him. His bones told him to get him out of there. But he patted his rump. "Go get 'em."

As soon as he got to the dugout he used the phone to instruct the bullpen to get Kunz, his knuckleballer, and Pasquale, his righthander, up and throwing.

Intimidated by Black's calm, color, and past success against him, Baxley pitched cautiously and without confidence and walked him on five pitches.

Now the infield was back, and Baxley was looking in at Shepley with Cheese Sorenson on deck. The Rube was not intimidated. He blew a low fast ball right through Shepley's swing. Shepley was not intimidated, either. He hit the next pitch on top of the right-field roof, about where Dandy's drive had gone, for four runs. The six-run lead was a two-run lead, and there were no outs in the inning.

Barney had been right in his bones, but his bones had not done the talking.

"Ladies and gentlemen," the field announcer's

voice informed the anguished crowd, "that was the ninth grandslam home run of Johnny Shepley's career and his third of the season."

Barney, making a sign to summon Pasquale, was on his way out to Baxley. "It helps to know that no bum hit it off of you."

A league rule required that a manager's second trip to the mound in an inning must result in a change of pitchers, so the Rube knew he was through. "I wish you hadn't come out, Skip. I still got two runs. I can hold 'em."

Barney took the ball and waited for his new pitcher. Gringo Pasquale was a mean Mexican. He had been playing professional ball for ten years, and he was only twenty-four years old. He was born old and strong and mean, and he had developed those qualities with age. Pasquale knew the hitters. What was there to say?

Barney gave him the ball and followed Baxley to the dugout, four steps back so as not to seem to share in the applause that went up for his retiring pitcher.

Now that the game was again in issue on every pitch, Barney returned to his corner and watched calmly. Pasquale missed low and outside, threw a high one that the Swede had to dive under, and then got him to chase a dropping curve. Sorenson's quick wrists got the bat on the ball, a bounder up the middle. Granny Wolf, whose sure hands could handle anything they could reach, did not get his glove all the way down, and the ball went between his legs and into center field. It was an error Granny did not make once in five years.

There were still no outs, and Amacito was at bat. He was no problem for Pasquale. He hit a comfortable grounder on an outside pitch to Sandowski's left at third. The big fellow made a nice play and threw accurately and in good faith at second base. Wolf, running to his left, intercepted the ball over the bag to force Sorensen. His job now was to leap to avoid Sorenson's take-out slide and, in the same motion, throw the ball with power across to first base to complete the double play. In his younger years Granny had made this difficult leaping pivot throw better than any player in the game at the time. He needed his young strength and coordination now, because Sorenson, a football player at heart, was coming at him with the roughest take-out slide in baseball. Granny was up and in the act of throwing a split second too late. Sorenson's slide cut him down. His throw went wild past Messengale.

As he watched Amacito pound into second base ahead of Messengale's recovery and throw, Barney wondered if Timmy Brooks would have been able to make the play that Granny had just missed.

The Swede, all goodhearted fellow player now,

offered Granny a hand up. On his feet unaided, Granny turned his cold eyes on Sorenson and cursed him. His use of profanity and obscenity was forceful, but not imaginative or interesting.

"Don't worry about him," Pasquale called to Granny. "I take care of him next time up."

Sorenson was hooted and booed until he disappeared into the dugout, and the crowd implored Pasquale to hold them.

So here we are, leading by 7 to 5 in the sixth inning, one out—Barney stood at the dugout rail and reminded his entire team that there was one out—with Amacito, not a fast runner, on second base (a fielder's choice and an error on Wolf on the throw), and Perdowski, a righthanded batter, at the plate. Pasquale threw his fast ball by him on the inside. Perdowski fouled the next pitch, also an inside fast ball, and was called out on the third pitch, a low outside fast ball.

Barney began to feel that he had a pitcher out there. There was only McStay to get this inning, and Briscoe would have the bottom of his line-up to start the seventh.

Pasquale curved a low strike in to McStay and followed it with a low fast ball that McStay hit as a bounder to Wade, who had a choice between charging the hop or stepping back to handle it high. He stepped back, and the ball hit the heel of his glove and got past him for another error. So the Warriors were still alive with Amacito at third and McStay at first. Now the lead run was at the plate in Bear Anderson, who hit twelve or fifteen home runs a year.

Pasquale calmly pitched over Wade's mistake and got Anderson to hit a routine fly ball to left. Dandy, playing a few steps in as instructed, had to go back a few steps for it. On the way back, somehow or other—the way things go in a bad inning—he stumbled, one foot tripping the other, and fell, and the ball dropped behind him. Both runs scored, and Anderson was on second.

The record of the game would show that Crum, whose defensive inabilities and mistakes had contributed most to the collapse of the Blue Jays' defense, had played errorless baseball. His home run would be a star in his crown forever. Some players get the breaks in the book, and some do not.

The crowd was tense and unhappy. The sudden blows of fate and the Warriors had turned a happy laugher into a desperate battle.

The Warriors had batted around in the inning, and Briscoe now was able to send up another pinch-hitter in the pitcher's position, to try to drive in Anderson with the lead run. Barney glanced at the roster card.

Briscoe was not in much better shape for right-handed batting strength on his bench than he was for lefthanded. Barney guessed he would send up Fisk, his reliable utility infielder and a good clutch hitter. He did.

Pasquale—now aggrieved, angry, grim, mean, and confident—dizzied Fisk with two slow curve balls, the second as slow as a girl's toss at a Sunday-school picnic, and then let him see the third strike after it blew past him.

The inning of disaster—six runs on only three hits —had created a new game. Getting up to go forth into it, Barney counted his blessings, as people do after they have lost their fortunes: one, Pasquale, pitching at his best, would have the support of the Blue Jays' best defense, as tight a defense as there was in baseball; two, the Warriors had three innings at bat left in a nine-inning game, while the Blue Jays had four; three, in this inning coming up, Barney's left-handed batting power would have another shot at Briscoe's righthanded pitching. So Barney, with a clap of his hands for his heroes, went forth.

The pitcher Briscoe sent out to the mound was not Massucci, the righthander; it was Fat Willie Mc-Donald, the lefthander with the dipsy-doodle knuckle ball.

Barney saw too late to the bottom of Briscoe's mind. The simplicity and power of Briscoe's strategy hit him harder than Shepley's grandslam home run. He had been fooled out of his fat lead, his game, the end of his losing streak—perhaps everything.

Briscoe had put his righthanded pitchers up as bait to tempt Barney into keeping his lefthanded hitters in the game. Briscoe had known he could not reasonably hope to overcome the big lead against the Blue Jays' best defense; his best chance for enough runs to get back in the game was to take advantage of the defensive weakness of Barney's power line-up. Briscoe had risked—and given up— two additional runs by coming in with righthanded pitching against the lefthanded power. But he had reckoned correctly. Barney had waited an inning too long before making his defensive changes.

Barney had had the game won. With a seven-run lead and his best defense, he could have locked it up. He had failed. His failure was more consequential and inexcusable than all the errors of commission and omission made on the field of play. He stood in his box, watching his toe kick at the line, afraid to look at his bench of players, lest they read on his face his shame and the certainty of defeat he deserved and would bring upon them.

Hochstein discovered a broken shoelace and called for time to replace it. It was a stall to give Fat Willie, who had not thrown in the bullpen, a few extra warm-up tosses.

Barney did not object. He needed the time more than Fat Willie. Another thought hit him: he had just made the most awful mistake of his life in front of a multitude, but nobody really knew it except the man who had maneuvered him into it. Behind him his bench was chattering encouragement to Dandy Crum, who was picking out a bat that could flatten a knuckleball. The crowd was anticipating action and drama. The voices of the venders were raised for beer and peanuts.

I've got to play over this mistake, Barney told himself. That is what there was to it. How many times, man and boy, manager and player, had he not said that in baseball, you have got to play over mistakes—yours and your teammates'? It is simple but tough. You have got to be able to play over the mistakes.

All right, Barney baby, play over this one.

He clapped his hands and took a look at his game. Should he let Crum, who was coming to the plate, hit for himself or should he send up Jeff Jones, the righthanded batter who would replace him in the field? (Now that Briscoe had gone with lefthanded pitching, Barney would keep Ted Jones on the bench against the need for a lefthanded pinch-hitter.) No, let Crum hit for himself: he deserved another shot at a fence, and the crowd, which was chanting in unison for another home run, deserved

a final look at the old hero who giveth you runs in
the bottom of the inning and taketh them away in
the top.

Fat Willie's ball was a jumping bean in the heavy
air. Crum struck out. Wolf grounded out. Sandowski struck out.

Briscoe knew what he was doing.

	1	2	3	4	5	6	7	8	9	R	H	E
WARRIORS	0	0	0	0	1	6				7	4	1
BLUE JAYS	2	1	1	3	0	0				7	11	6

Barney called for Jeff Jones to go to right field,
with Wellington moving to left; for Brooks to take
second, and for Tuffson to take third base. These
changes gave him this line-up:

Messengale, 1B
J. Jones, RF
Brooks, 2B
Tuffson, 3B
Slater, C
Wilkins, CF
Wellington, LF
Wade, SS
Pasquale, P

11

There were a shower, a beer, a sandwich, a smoke, and a radio for Dandy Crum and Sandy Sandowski in the clubhouse, but they stayed in the dugout to watch. Wolf was still in the game as a coach.

Big Don Norman walked into the dugout. He had draped a warm-up jacket over the sling in which his plastered-up left elbow rested. He was still in uniform, back to watch. The bench paraded over to him as if he had come in after hitting a home run, to shake his hand and get the word direct that it was just a chip, he'd be back in the line-up in a week.

"I haven't heard one of our games on the air since I sprained my ankle that time in Cincinnati," he told Barney. "People all over town are listenin'. In cars. At the hospital. All pullin' for us."

"I wish I had you the rest of the way."

They watched Messengale throw Big Don's stained practice ball to the infielders. "Too bad he can't play regular," Big Don said.

Gringo Pasquale did not throw his first pitch at
Baxley's ancient enemy, Hochstein the Horn; he
served up a big lollipop of a curve that Hochstein
was so surprised to see that he did nothing but
watch it. His next pitch was a still slower curve
that Hochstein chased too soon. With two strikes
on him, Gringo threw at him and made him sit
down. The Blue Jay bench laughed at Hochstein's
rage, because, with two strikes, he could not waste
a strike throwing his bat or trying to bunt down
the first-base line and walking up Gringo's back.
The Mex fired a low outside fast ball. Hochstein
had to protect the plate and, swinging hard, topped
a grounder down the third-base line. It was rolling
for a hit. Tuffson snatched it bare-handed and made
a running throw at Messengale. It was off the bag.
Messengale stretched and got it as Hochstein
flashed across the bag—and was called out by
Snorkel Mintz. Hochstein, Mike Kista (the first-
base coach), and Briscoe, charging from the dugout
like a killer buffalo, stormed and hollered to
strengthen their argument that Messengale had
been pulled off the bag. While the crowd yelled
derision, Briscoe stalked the other umpires in vain
appeals. The more Kista argued about it, the more
righteous he became. Advancing on Mintz, he
bumped him with his chest, and Mintz, with a
thrust of the thumb, ordered him out of the game.

The Blue Jays (especially Baxley, who had also stayed in the dugout) enjoyed the Warriors' unhappiness and frustration as much as the crowd did.

Billy Smith came in to coach at first base, and Gringo pitched to Tony Black. He hit the first pitch, a good fast ball, to right center. Jeff Jones ran hard and dove and slid twice his length, trying to get his glove under the falling ball, but it was an inch or two short. The ball bounded past him. Wilkins, in on the play, swung around to back it up. Black, going for second when he saw the ball get by Jones, saw Wilkins' quick low throw and knew he was out at second unless he could knock the ball out of Brooks's grasp with a hard slide. Brooks caught the ball at bag level and swung to ram it into Black's spikes. Black was out, and the crowd cheered, but Black's spikes had torn a gash across the knuckle of the index finger of Brooks's right hand. He stood looking at the blood.

Barney felt the calamitous nature of the injury in his heart and belly as he ran out, followed by Hank, to look at the boy's hand.

"It may not be as bad as it looks," he said as Hank examined the wound.

"It's cut to the bone," Hank said. "Needs a stitch or two. The knucklebone could be cracked."

Timmy tried to work the finger. There was no strength in it. "Tape it," he said. "I can throw."

"Can he throw?" Barney asked Hank.

"He can't throw," Hank said. "If it is broke," he said to Barney, "we got to take care of it, or he may never throw any more."

Barney put his hand on the boy's shoulder. "Hank and Doc will fix you up, Timmy."

"You don't have an infielder on the bench," the boy said.

"Get Ted Jones out here," Barney ordered as Brooks walked to the dugout, a perfectly tuned athletic machine made useless by a small broken part.

Barney called his coaches into a conference around the bag. "Ted played infield part of one year at Allentown."

"So did Wilkins," Jinx said. "He played short nearly a full season for Decatur the year before he went to Spokane."

"You know, Barney, I was thinking," Cronkite put in. "Messengale at second. Put Ted on first."

"He can handle the ground ball," Granny said, "but he throws left, and Ted throws right."

"Ted could play first okay," Tate said.

"How about Wilkins at second," Barney said, "and Ted in left and Wellington to center?"

"I don't see we could do better," Granny said.

"Okay?" Barney asked. They all nodded. "Get the line-up straight with the umpires," he told Cronkite.

Messengale, 1B
J. Jones, RF
T. Jones, LF
Tuffson, 3B
Slater, C
Wilkins, 2B
Wellington, CF
Wade, SS
Pasquale, P

"I remind you," Barney told his players as they huddled, "that all we got left on the bench is pitchers and catchers. You better last."

The field announcer's voice called out the nature of the injury and the line-up changes, and a muted roar in which exhortation of its own heroes was more dominant than damnation of the enemy came from the crowd. The grand victory was turning into the kind of defeat the gods hand down.

Paulson the sportswriter and the old professor from the University of Chicago, introduced by Tom Poole, were side by side in the back row of the press box.

"Barney brought his troubles on himself," Paulson remarked, "by his reckless use of players in getting Adams out of there."

" 'Troubles come upon my people like a river,' " the old professor said, after Aeschylus.

Pasquale still had Shepley to get out. As the devil would have it, Shepley hit sharply on the ground toward right center. Wilkins got in front of the ball, fumbled it, picked it up quickly, and threw to Messengale—an instant too late. The pressure of baseball had burst Barney's infield at its only untested place. Wilkins had kicked his first chance; Shepley was safe at first; the Warriors were still alive in the inning; Cheese Sorenson was at the plate.

Pasquale rubbed the ball and turned to Wilkins. "No harm done, kid." Having eased the tension of a teammate, Pasquale turned to increase it in an enemy, Cheese Sorenson.

Shepley was prancing off first, eager for the jump that would give him a chance to score on any long ball the Big Swede might hit. Sorenson expected a ball at his head. Seeming to ignore Shepley's dancing lead, Pasquale threw quickly to Messengale, whose swooping tag caught Shepley in his dive back. Abruptly the inning was over. "You still got yours coming, Cheesehead," Pasquale called to Sorenson.

The crowd, cheering the play, rose for its seventh-inning stretch and applauded Wilkins as he ran to the dugout. With a good word from Pasquale and a hand from the crowd, the only thing Wilkins could think was that he'd better get a hit and not kick any more ground balls.

Fat Willie had been with seven clubs in both leagues in his seventeen years as a major-league pitcher. He had a big belly, a loud mouth, an untiring arm, and weak legs. He did not beat himself.

Slater went up there to wear him down. He took the bad pitches and pounded the good ones foul until he had a 3-2 count. Fat Willie came in with his best pitch, a floating knuckle ball that dipped. Slater swung and missed as the ball sank sharply. Anderson tried to smother it, but it got past him, and Slater made first base ahead of the throw, on a strikeout and a passed ball.

This is our inning. Barney knew it. He had his three best righthanded batters coming up—Wilkins, Wellington, and Wade. He had Caluga on the bench to hit for Pasquale. *Play this one right, baby—play it right.*

Briscoe knew it. Massucci, his righthander, was already loose in the bullpen. Buzzy Benz, another righthander, and Curt Randolph, a lefthander, got up and began to throw.

Barney called to Tate in the bullpen to see that

Harry Kunz, the lefthanded knuckleballer, and Joe Kerwin, the hardest-throwing righthander on the squad, got ready.

The action in both bullpens whetted the crowd's realization that the game was rising to its climax. "Go! Go! Go!" The unified chant pounded with Barney's pulse.

He needed wheels on first base. The fastest runner on his bench was young Bobby Martin, a pitcher. He called to the dugout, and the boy came bounding out and ran to take Slater's place. Slater trotted back to the bench, a hero of the game.

Barney gave Wilkins the bunt-and-run sign. Briscoe knew it. Sorenson and Amacito moved down the lines; Fat Willie knew it and kept his first two pitches high, too high. Two balls and no strikes. Barney gave Wilkins the take sign to test Fat Willie's control. But Briscoe was taking no chances on the knuckleballer's control. He came out quickly and called for Massucci. The tension was prolonged and intensified for the crowd as Gino Massucci walked in and took his warm-up pitches.

With two balls and no strikes, he could not waste a pitch. He would throw a high strike—if he could. Could he? Barney repeated the take sign. The pitch was high and a little outside. Now he had to come in with a strike—a strike down the middle, since Wilkins would be taking anyway. Why take?

Barney gave the take sign—and gave it again. Take-on-take takes take off. He gave the bunt-and-run sign. It was a perfect pitch to bunt, and Wilkins dragged it perfectly. Amacito made the play to first with Massucci covering, but Martin was on second with the lead run in scoring position. Barney and the Blue Jays and the fans called upon Wellington to bring it home.

He came through—a sharp ground single between McStay and Sorenson into left field. Perdowski charged the ball swiftly, and Barney held Martin up at third. There were runners on first and third, only one out, and Wade was at bat.

Briscoe came out and talked it over with his pitcher and the infield. Pasquale was due next. There were only two pinch-hitters on the Blue Jays' bench —the two catchers. Barney would almost certainly choose Caluga, who would stay in the line-up to replace Slater behind the plate. Caluga was a left-handed batter who had never hit Massucci well. Besides, he was a slow runner and would be an easy double play if he hit the ball on the ground.

Briscoe decided to walk Wade and load the bases. The crowd howled its scorn and anger, but Barney knew that Briscoe had made a move that thrust deeply into the weakness that Barney had created by the strength he had used to destroy Jerry Adams. If Crum, Sandowski, Wolf, or Ted Jones had been available on his bench, Briscoe would have had to pitch to Wade.

Now what, Barney baby? What do you do now? You squeeze it home. You should have squeezed it home last night. So squeeze it home today.

Who?

Caluga? Young Michaels? Too slow, both too slow. Pasquale? How about Pasquale? Not too good a bunter, but very fast. Besides, he's your pitcher. If you do get the run home, he can hold 'em for you. If you don't get the run home, he'd better hold 'em for you. It's his game.

Pasquale was already on the way to the plate, swinging two bats as if he were going up there to give himself a four-run lead.

With Pasquale the batter, the Warriors prepared to defend against the squeeze—infield in and Sorenson and Amacito poised to charge down the lines. Confidence left Barney; the play that had seemed certain to succeed only a moment ago now seemed certain to fail. He felt that Briscoe, who was merely responding to his move, had outmaneuvered him again. *Get Caluga up there; he can hit you the scoring fly.*

Instead, as if he were already committed, he gave the bunt-and-run sign. Massucci fired it in high, as Pasquale squared around and Martin broke for home. The bat met the ball and popped it gently and di-

rectly into Massucci's glove. A leisurely toss to Mc-
Stay, covering third, completed the double play. The
inning and the Blue Jays' best hope for victory
were stamped into the past. Barney walked to the
dugout, and the boos of the crowd were on his head.

	1	2	3	4	5	6	7	8	9	R	H	E
WARRIORS	0	0	0	0	1	6	0			7	5	1
BLUE JAYS	2	1	1	3	0	0	0			7	12	7

Caluga went in to catch.

Pasquale did not believe in his own vulnerability.
He went back out to the mound brooding about his
failure to squeeze the run home. Going to the plate,
he had felt deep confidence that he was going to
drive one or two runs home, maybe all three. When
he had got the bunt sign, he had reckoned the run
as good as home. He found it difficult to believe that
he had popped the ball into an easy double play.

Almost abstractedly he threw at Sorenson's head,
then at his legs to insult him. He made him dive, and
he made him dance. He figured to get him out with
his curve, but the Cheesehead somehow got good
wood on it, and it would have gone for two bases
sure if Wilkins hadn't leaped high and come down
with it. That made up for the one he had booted.

Amacito hit the ball well toward the right-field

corner, but the wind took it foul, and Pasquale got him to hit on the ground to the new kid on first who could cover more ground than Big Don.

So it was an easy inning because Perdowski was lucky to hit a fly ball to right that Jeff Jones jumped up and caught before it could hit the screen and bounce around for a couple of bases.

As the Blue Jays trotted in for their bats, the fans applauded the three fine defensive plays that had cut down the Warriors. Then they chanted for action from the top of the Blue Jay line-up.

Barney met Wilkins at the line. "Way to go." He turned to meet Messengale coming in from first. "Way to go." And he waited for Jeff Jones trotting in from right. "Way to go."

He told himself the game could still be won. Even his bad breaks had not been all bad. He needed Big Don's bat, but he was stronger defensively with the kid at first. He needed Brooks's defensive play, but he was stronger offensively with four outfielders in the batting line-up. He had a good chance this inning with a good mixture of power and speed— Messengale, a lefty; Jeff Jones, a rightie; and Ted Jones, a switcher.

He had more than a chance, more than a good chance. He could feel it in his bones: they were going to win this one and they were going to keep on winning—win two for every one they lost—and they were going to sweep right on to the pennant. They were a team. He had a team. They were going to win, and this was the inning.

He clapped his hands and called to Messengale to get it started. The kid got behind on the count and lifted a high foul to the first baseman.

"Up to you, Jeff. Up to you. Get it started."

But Jeff, swinging for a fence, topped an easy roller to Sorenson.

"C'mon, Ted, get a hold o' one."

Ted, batting lefthanded against Massucci, swung at the first pitch and lifted a soaring fly to right center. It hung way up there and drifted in the wind. Tony Black was against the wall, waiting for a ball that never came down. It landed on the roof for a home run. The Blue Jays were ahead 8 to 7. The crowd was no more jubilant than Barney and the Blue Jays' bench, which was waiting to pound Ted when he came in. Barney grabbed his hand and whacked his rump as he went by. There was a certain look in Ted's quick smile, of triumph: the Old Liner, the last man on the bench, had not failed the man who had put him down. Barney looked after him and watched the joyous mob in the dugout work him over. In baseball you never learned enough to feel you knew enough. "We got a team," Barney said to the exuberant air. "Keep it going, Tuffy," he called to the next batter, and the kid did, a clean drive past McStay for a single. But Caluga, going for distance, undercut the ball slightly and raised an easy fly to center.

	1	2	3	4	5	6	7	8	9	R	H	E
WARRIORS	0	0	0	0	1	6	0	0		7	5	1
BLUE JAYS	2	1	1	3	0	0	0	1		8	14	7

So it was up to Pasquale to hold the lead against the Warriors in the ninth inning, their last chance to tie it up or go ahead.

With the bottom of his line-up coming up, Briscoe looked to his bench. He had two good righthanded batters, Costello, his third catcher, who hit with power, and Higgins, a pitcher, who was one of his most reliable pinch-hitters; and two lefthanders, Ates, an alternate outfielder, and young Branstadt, his utility infielder, who was hitting a strong .300.

Briscoe sent McStay up, in turn, to lead it off. Jinx, watching Briscoe, called out the bunt possibility, and Tuffson and Messengale edged in against it. Pasquale pitched him a high curve. McStay turned into the ball as if to bunt, but took it for a ball as both Tuffson and Messengale charged. Pasquale fired a high slider. McStay swung away and drilled the ball on a line to left field, where Ted Jones was waiting for it. One out and two to go. Only two more.

Briscoe sent Higgins to the plate. Pasquale missed with two low fast balls, got the third one in there, missed with a low curve, and walked him with another fast ball. With his tying run on first, Briscoe sent up Branstadt, the fastest man on his squad, to hit for Anderson. The hit-and-run was on. Trying to pull a low outside fast ball, Branstadt met the ball squarely and drove it through the hole over second for a ground single. Wellington was in fast and kept Wiggins from going to third. But the tying run had moved like doom to scoring position. *Still* two outs to go. The air was too heavy to breathe.

Briscoe came in with his power hitter, Nick Costello, a veteran who had come through with as many clutch hits as any man in the game. Briscoe had the right man at the right time.

The Gringo Kid, poised like a killer, studied him calmly, accepted the sign from Caluga, and brushed him back with a fast ball. Then he dropped his lollipop curve in on him. Hitting the ball too close to his fists, Costello stroked a sinking liner back of second. Wilkins, who could go back, went back and brought it down with a leaping catch.

Now only one to go. C'mon, Gringo, only one. *They let you get this close, they gotta let you in.* Not in baseball. In baseball the hero can be the other guy. Hochstein the Horn, an avenger with a long cry of injustices, stood at the plate.

Pasquale fired a fast ball inside and missed with a low fast ball outside. He came in with a beautiful curve that Hochstein chose to take for strike one. Pasquale, the marksman, shot him with another more beautiful curve just above the knees that cut the plate like an arrow in a Valentine heart for strike two. But Shaughnessy called it ball three.

The Blue Jays jumped up to yell their rage. Barney could not believe the call. "I won't take it!" he screamed at Shaughnessy and advanced toward him. The bad call had uncorked Gringo's temper, and he charged toward the plate in red rage. Caluga leaped in front of the plate with widespread arms to wrap him in a hug and cool him down. Barney, responding to the discipline of the game and his quick fear that both he and Pasquale would be kicked out, changed his course and ran to help his big catcher hold his little pitcher.

Shaughnessy, whose own temper was roused by the tumultuous booing from the stands, stood poised to end the demonstration on the field with the getout signal. He hesitated the instant that gave Barney and Caluga a chance to head their pitcher back to the mound.

"Bad call, kid," Barney crooned, "pitch over it. Pitch over it, baby."

"You can do it," Caluga told him. "Blow your fast ball past him." He gave him the ball.

Pasquale took a deep breath. "Okay. Play ball."

Barney looked at him, patted his back, and went back to his pilothouse.

But Pasquale's next pitch went low for ball four, and the bases were loaded for Tony Black.

Kerwin and Kunz were warmed up and ready to go. Kerwin was a fast-ball pitcher and Tony was a fast-ball hitter. Kunz was a lefthanded knuckle-baller, and Tony lived and got well on lefthanded pitching. Barney needed Pasquale and his curve ball in there to get the last out.

The first pitch was a low fast ball into the dirt. Caluga just did block it as Higgings charged down the line and then hustled back to third. Tony watched the next pitch, a high curve, float in and down for strike one. And he watched the next one float by on the outside for ball two.

Pasquale called for a new ball, rubbed it carefully, and dusted his fingers with the resin bag. He had to come in with a strike—and a strike with something on it. He came in with a quick slider that caught the outside corner at the knees.

Shaughnessy called it ball three.

Caluga, the peacemaker of a minute before, leaped around to confront Shaughnessy with curses that fed his own rage. He bumped Shaughnessy with his chest and followed the reeling umpire back and stepped on his feet. By the time Barney got there, Caluga was out of the game. He wheeled Caluga toward the dugout and called for young Michaels, his third catcher, to get his gear on.

"It was there, Skip. It was *there*," Caluga kept saying, and the big man was crying.

Barney looked at Pasquale, standing slumped like the last Indian. Was he relaxed or defeated? There were three balls and one strike on Tony Black. Could he count on the Gringo Kid to fire a strike, two if necessary? He could not. Kunz, his knuckleballer was ready. But you can't risk a knuckleball when you need a strike. It had to be Joe Kerwin. Joe was a fast-ball pitcher. Tony was a fast-ball hitter. But it had to be Joe.

He walked to the mound and raised his right hand as the signal to Joe.

"It's my game, Skip," Pasquale said. "Let me keep the ball."

They all wanted to play. They were all heroes, as in the olden days of Greece. "We'll let Joe wrap it up for you, Gringo," Barney said, holding the ball he had taken from Caluga.

The crowd was in a delirium of agony as Kerwin came on. Young Michaels and the infielders came to the mound to wait for him. The ball game and everything everybody had put into it would be riding on Joe's pitch. When Joe stepped on the mound, Pasquale said, "You're the man, Joe," and walked to the dugout.

Joe Kerwin was a loner. Who knew him? He was tall and skinny. His hands were big and his arms hung loose and long. He was homeless. Whatever club he belonged to, he lived in a cheap rooming-house or efficiency apartment as near to the park as possible. He liked to walk to work. On the road, he was always in his hotel room when he was not required to be with the club.

He did not have a third pitch, and his second pitch, his curve, was unreliable, but he could throw strikes like seeds all day long.

The way it works in baseball, sometimes everything rides on a man you never saw before and may never see again, a man without a beginning or an end, a man of one moment of your time, to be able to do the right thing.

"You know the count?" Barney asked Kerwin.

"Three and one, ain't it?"

"If you throw low, it might go too low. Fire it down the middle."

"He'll be waitin' for it."

"Maybe he'll hit it at somebody."

"Maybe he won't hit it at all."

Barney gave him the ball and left him out there alone.

Joe took his warm-up tosses easily, more with the idea of warming up Michaels than getting himself ready. He was always ready. That was his business, and he would be working at it for a long time, with one club or another.

They were ready to play.

Joe went through all the motions—looking in, getting the sign, getting set, checking the runner on third. . . . Then he fired it in there.

Tony Black swung, and the sound of bat on ball rang with the solid connection of the mighty drive to left center.

Wellington, playing in as instructed, turned and fled with the flight of the ball. It was over his head when he and it reached the wall together. He leaped, twisting, high against the wall and fell heavily back with the ball in his glove in the moment of silence.

12

Barney stood rear guard in front of the dugout. His players, pounding Wellington and Kerwin and Ted Jones and each other, were storming down the tunnel and over the bridge and into the clubhouse. He wanted to be with them.

Tom Poole was in front of him with a corps of writers and photographers. "Two quick things, Barney. Everybody wants pictures and interviews in the clubhouse. You'd think we had just won the World Series."

"In five minutes. Keep everybody out of the clubhouse for five minutes."

"What are you going to tell them, Barney?" a writer asked.

"Thanks," Barney said.

"It'll be five minutes, fellows," Tom called to the press people.

"Who would you say were the stars of the game?" another writer persisted.

"Every man on the club was in this game," Barney

said, "and all the coaches. Later. You can talk to them all later."

"You used your entire roster, except for a few pitchers."

"That's right," Barney said.

"Michaels got in the game for one pitch, and didn't handle the ball," somebody said.

"He was there," Barney said.

"The other thing, Barney," Tom said, "those visiting intellectuals want another session with you tomorrow. They want to talk about today's game."

"No," Barney said. It was not his game to talk about. "I'm taking my kids to the zoo tomorrow."

"Do you think this win is the end of your losing streak?" a writer asked.

"This is a winning ball club," Barney said.

"How bad are you hurt until Norman and Brooks are back in the line-up?"

"This is a winning ball club," Barney repeated.

Johnston Dudley and his sister Lissie were in front of him.

"Congratulations, Barney. A great game, most exciting I ever saw."

Barney took his hand. "Thanks, Johnse. They battled through."

"We got a big one to celebrate tonight. And you've got an open date tomorrow."

"I haven't asked any of them yet, Johnse."

"Get the right ones there, Barney," Lissie said. "We're counting on you."

"I can't ask any of them without asking all of them," Barney said.

"All of them! We can't handle the whole club, Barney," Lissie said.

"It's your club. You come in and ask who you want. I can't do it."

"Ask them all to stop by for a drink," Johnston said. "I'll call the caterers. They can handle it."

"I want to meet them all," the fading lady said. "Especially the one who made the last catch."

"I'll ask them all," Barney said.

He looked for Marianna. Her box was empty. He wanted to say a word to his players and get on home. He turned and ran down the dark tunnel.

	1	2	3	4	5	6	7	8	9		R	H	E
WARRIORS	0	0	0	0	1	6	0	0	0		7	6	1
BLUE JAYS	2	1	1	3	0	0	0	1			8	14	7